Between 1961 and 1963, Alvin Currier studied Marxism at the Free University of Berlin. At the same time, he worked as part of an informal ecumenical service group that took responsibility for information and contacts with the East. In almost daily trips to East Berlin he met many of the leaders of the church there and acted as translator and guide for many American churchmen. He also spent two years as a German pastor. Since being appointed in 1964 to his present position as assistant chaplain at Macalester College, St. Paul, Minn., he has returned twice for extended study trips in Eastern Europe.

# NO EASTER
# FOR
# EAST GERMANY?

# NO EASTER FOR EAST GERMANY?

BY ALVIN C. CURRIER

AUGSBURG PUBLISHING HOUSE
MINNEAPOLIS, MINNESOTA

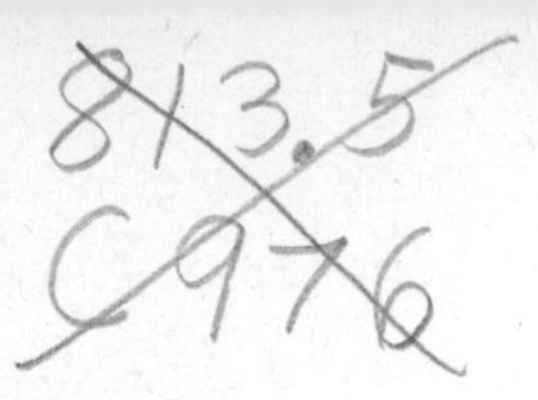



NO EASTER FOR EAST GERMANY?



Library of Congress Catalog Card No. 68-13424

Manufactured in the United States of America

## DEDICATION

# To My Wife

Wenn ich alle Weiber der Welt ansehe, so finde ich keine, von der ich rühmen könnte, wie ich von meiner mit fröhlichem Gewissen rühmen kann; diese hat mir Gott selbst geschenkt, und ich weiss, dass Ihm samt allen Engeln wohlgefällt, wenn ich mit Liebe und Treue zu ihr halte.

Luther concerning Katie

*English translation*

When I look at all the women of the world, I find none that I can praise, as with a joyful heart I praise my own; for God himself has given her to me and I know that it pleases him and all the angels when I hold to her in love and truth.

# FOREWORD

In May of 1960, before the erection of the Wall, I had the privilege of spending a week in East Berlin at a time when it was still relatively easy to travel back and forth between East and West. I use the word "privilege" advisedly, for I emerged from that week in the company of East German churchmen with a new picture of the task and possibilities of the church in our day, along with a new appreciation for the kind of quiet courage involved simply in being the church in a land that is against many things for which the church stands.

But this exposure to East German Christianity was also devastating. For in East Germany it costs to be a churchman, and since churchmanship in the West is not costly, the inevitable comparisons to our complacent Western ecclesiasticism were not particularly flattering. If I left East Berlin proud to be a Christian and a churchman, the pride was based more on what other churches were doing than on what we in the West were doing.

Such an impression, however, is open to radical misinterpretation. For I am not saying that we should feel sorry for Christians behind the Iron Curtain. That shoe, indeed, may fit on the other foot, and many East Germans expressed pity for those of us so trapped in the structures of the "culture-Protestantism" of the West, one girl going as far as to say, in reflecting on a recent trip to Switzerland, "I think it is easier to be a Christian in East Germany than in Switzerland."

There is something wonderful about the depth of commitment that emerges when the church cannot be "taken for granted," particularly when it is coupled with a kind of Christian freedom that comes from being made radically aware, as one is made in East Germany, that many of the past structures of the church may be totally inadequate for today's tasks, and may even impede rather than enhance the church's attempt to exist for the sake of the particular part of the world where God has placed it. One is not therefore called upon to pity East German Christians, but rather to hear what their experience is saying to us.

What their experience tells us is more applicable than we dare believe; the parallels for the church between the East German situation and the American situation are greater than we initially want to contemplate. It is true that East German Christians face active hostility, while American Christians face massive indifference. But with the recession of the "religious boom," our own increasing minority status is going to render many of our own structures inadequate to the tasks of the church tomorrow. The East German situation, in short, offers us, in bold and stark outline, a parable of what is increasingly becoming our own situation—a situation in which the church will count for less in our total national life rather than more, a situation in which our numbers are going to decrease rather than increase in proportion to the total population, and a situation in which many on the periphery of church life will drop away rather than be drawn farther in. Thus we need to learn about the church in East Germany, not only to become acquainted with its situation, but also to learn from it for our situation.

Readers of this book are fortunate in being able to see the East German church through the eyes of Alvin Currier. At the conference I attended in East Berlin it was Mr. Currier who acted as interpreter between East and West, interpreting not only our various languages but also interpreting our different outlooks, so that we were brought closer to one another through him than we could possibly have been without him. The gulf between us was initially very deep, and it could have become even deeper had we not had in Mr. Currier one who could enter sympathetically into the viewpoint of those both in East and West and help us all, through a week of intensive conversation, to come to understand one another better.

This is also what his book does for the reader. And however ill-informed, distorted, or extravagant may be our present assessment of the church in East Germany, we cannot read these pages without being deeply moved, and even deeply threatened, as well as being finally renewed, by what we learn from them.

Robert McAfee Brown

Stanford University

# PREFACE

The Wall was built in August, 1961. Less than a month later I arrived in Berlin for nearly three years of study as a student at the Free University and later as pastor of a German church.

During those days in Berlin following the disruption of communications caused by the Wall, I went back and forth between West and East Berlin through Checkpoint Charlie literally hundreds of times on all sorts of errands for all sorts of people as well as for myself. I visited in countless homes. East German synod assemblies, diocese assemblies, consistorium meetings, church councils, study groups, house churches, retreats, and conferences became a part of my life. I guided hundreds of visitors through Berlin. I established deep friendships with people in many different positions on both sides of the Wall. In addition, while making these almost daily trips back and forth between East and West, I also studied German history and sociology at the University. This book is the result of all these experiences.

I have only one goal in these pages. My premise is that the story of the struggle of the church in East Germany is basically a human drama. Therefore I have attempted with these few vignettes to give the reader something of the "feel" of the stage, the script, the actors, and the emotion of that drama that is the subject of these pages.

Such a dramatic presentation is necessary to put the meat of reality onto the skeleton of historical analysis. Such a presentation is necessary to set the collections of apologetic writings in context. Such a presentation fills in the human pathos which cannot be caught by the lens of a camera.

The actors who speak in these stories are real people, with their names and circumstances only slightly disguised to avoid embarrassment. The scenario also was written by actual events and encounters. In fact, except for my own inevitable bias and the little bit of disguise necessary to shield those who cross these pages, this book may be considered non-fiction.

I hope that these encounters may demonstrate to many the rich and many-sided life of the church in East Germany.

ALVIN C. CURRIER

Macalester College

# CONTENTS

# PART ONE

# LIFE AND PROBLEMS OF EAST GERMANS

# THE WALLS

"Back in the days when there was no food I walked weeks on end from the shops to the post office to keep poor Gertrud alive over there. Oh, I don't know how many of the packages got lost or stolen by those Communists, but do you know, our food packages from here in the West to our loved ones in the East actually showed up in Cuba? The Communists stole them and sent them to Cuba. Oh, I know it, Herr Pastor. I heard from a very dear friend how she got a letter back written in Spanish thanking her for her gift."

My hostess continued.

"In East Berlin in those days you could get meat now and then if you were strong enough to stand in line, but in the country there was no meat for weeks on end. That's in the East, of course. No rice. No noodles. No potatoes. Pigs eating the tails and ears off each other, they were so hungry. Oh, my dear Herr Pastor, you have no idea what horrors our poor homeland is suffering."

My hostess was a big woman, probably in her late fifties, and obviously given to the dramatic.

Early on this cold, rainy morning she had called me at my West Berlin apartment to ask whether I might consider taking a package over to East Berlin for her. I had been hesitant but at last I had consented. Package-carrying was part of the life of every foreigner in Berlin.

When I arrived at the apartment of my hostess she promptly ushered me into her parlor to tell me her story. It seems that my hostess has a very dear friend by the name of Gertrud who lives alone in East Berlin with her schoolteacher daughter Gretchen.

My hostess and her friend Gertrud had grown up together. They had visited each other constantly in the years before the war, and they had consoled each other during the hard war years when the men were away. Both of them had been widowed by the war. Then Berlin was divided. Gertrud lived in the Russian Sector and my hostess lived here in the American Sector, which later became part of West Berlin. As the new post-war Germany took shape these two women clung even tighter to each other. Then the telephone service was cut off between West and East Berlin, and now the Wall had come, leaving them only the mails through which to console each other. The Wall was the last straw in a whole load of events that had shaken the life of my hostess: The fall of Germany. The loss of her husband. The hunger and disease of the immediate post-war years. The occupation. The blockade. The creation of the German Democratic Republic. The refugees. The Wall.

My hostess had mentally retreated from all this. Her apartment was a museum to the memory of a bygone era. Everywhere were velvet and cut glass. The coffee table and brandy table had marble tops. A dog lay in one corner, and a bird chirped in an ornate cage. Plants wound around the room, rooted in various pots. Bare spots on the wall were hung with pictures of very Kaiser-like ladies and gentlemen. A sensuous marble nude nymph stood atop a tall Corinthian marble pillar. In this setting my hostess had isolated herself from the clash and clamor of the present.

She realized that something had gone wrong in her life. As she poured me a brandy from her lovely cut glass decanter she knew it was not like in the old days. The solution to her problem, though, was simple: The Communists were to blame. They had built the Wall; they had separated her from Gertrud. Now she spilled out to me the stories that she had collected about them.

"The first sweater that I knitted for Gertrud never got there. Can you imagine the hours of knitting, Herr Pastor? Can you imagine people stealing mail just like that? That's why I had to ask you to take this second sweater over to East Berlin yourself and personally give it to my dear Gertrud."

I stood up to leave, and she gave me the package along with scattered remarks about God's mercy, the poor, and a rumored concentration camp in East Germany where she didn't think I would be sent if I got caught with the package.

If West Berlin had looked glum on this wet, dark morning, East Berlin looked like a tomb. I had no parking problem in front of Gertrud's apartment building. It was a building of the same vintage and style as that of her friends in West Berlin, but here in the East the streets were empty, and the leafless winter trees looked twice as bleak against the gray sky between the dark buildings. I lit my lighter to read the names on the mailboxes. Almost every apartment here was divided up for at least two families. Finally I found the name and started back for the door. I rang twice at the tall glass-paneled door and waited. Gertrud appeared. At first I didn't see her. The door was opened such a small crack that I wouldn't even have noticed that it was open if it hadn't squeaked. A tiny, shrill voice asked: "What do you want?"

I peered into the dark crack trying to see who or what was talking, and then I told the person behind the door the story of my mission. When I finished, the door suddenly opened wide, revealing another heavy-set, amply endowed woman, dressed in cottons and tweeds with ugly heavy flat shoes.

"Come in, come in," Gertrud squeaked as she hobbled with strange jerking motions across the hall to open the door to her living room. After opening the door to her parlor she returned to the front door to lock it and bolt it. The room was almost exactly the same as the room of my hostess in West Berlin as far as the size and shape went. Plants were everywhere, along with many Kaiser vintage pictures. The furniture was massive. The television was prominent and obviously in continuous use. Letters and envelopes lay scattered on the table.

"Would you prefer coffee or tea?" Gertrud asked as she returned, standing half bent over in front of me. I answered in favor of tea, knowing that coffee was scarce and four times as expensive as in West Berlin.

I found a place among the pillows on the sofa. As I sat waiting in the dark room my eyes noticed a big pile of magazines. I got up out of the sofa and took the liberty of turning on a light before I examined the magazines. I was astonished. All of the magazines were years old and all of them were from the West. They had been bought before the Wall. I began to look around the room for other signs like this that would tell me more about Gertrud and her daughter Gretchen.

Postcards from Western and foreign resorts were laid out to be seen. I took note of that. Pictures standing between pictures on the top of the piano testified to many relatives in the West. At least in some of the pictures the cut of the clothes made it obvious that they were Western.

Gertrud came back into the room with a large wooden tray loaded with a teapot, three cups, sugar, and a plate of goodies. I was reading a 1960 copy of "Das Bild."

"Oh, that's our lifeline," squeaked Gertrud. "That and TV."

After the tea was spread on the coffee table Gertrud flopped down with an awkward motion into the chair in front of the television that was clearly hers. With a couple of jerks she moved it around to half face me. Then she took up the bag with the sweater in it and lovingly took it out. Gertrud wasn't much of a woman, but it was moving to see the way she held and felt and admired the sweater. It was more than just a nice piece of clothing. It was a lovely gift from a dear friend, but even more than that, it was something from the West—from the other side—a vision—a sign—from that other place where there is no more crying, neither are there tears any more. Gertrud sat feeling the sweater as if it were alive, and then she began to pour out her feelings as if some floodgate had given way.

"Oh, Herr Pastor, where would we be if it weren't for our dear friends? What did we do to deserve this? My man was an honest man. Rector of a modest Volksschool he was when the war broke out. A friend of all men. A God-fearing man. Some of our best friends were Jews. We thought it was just awful what happened to them, but what could my man do? Should he risk his job and leave all those children to the Nazis? Oh, we were never members of the Party. My man never joined a party. No, we stood strictly above all that. We were some of the last ones to leave the church, and it is still one of the heavy burdens that I have to carry in my old age—that is the knowledge that he died somewhere out there without last communion. I know he would have joined the church again if he had ever returned from the front. It's the only bulwark we have today against the Eastern heathen here in the Zone."

Gertrud's face was twisted in anguish as she flooded the room with words, but I had the horribly uneasy feeling that she enjoyed recounting her misery.

"Poor Gretchen suffered unmentionable atrocities at the hands of the Russians when they marched into Berlin. Since then she has devoted her life to teaching and caring for me. Poor girl. All the men were killed at the front. She never had a chance. And so horribly violated by the Russians."

The old woman looked up at me as if she wanted to make sure that I knew exactly what she was talking about. She seemed to feel compelled to dwell upon the behavior of the Russians but I assured her that I had heard over and over again the stories of the Russian entrance into Berlin.

"Oh, and then this ordeal began," the woman said, taking up her lament again. "We joined the church again, Herr Pastor. Gretchen and I did. We don't go any more now. Well, you see, with Gretchen and her job. She's a teacher you know—yes, I told you. Well, she'd be fired in a minute if she went to church. You have no idea. So we sit alone and suffer, cut off from the Word and the Holy Sacraments."

There was a rattle of bolts and jingle of keys out in the hall.

"That must be Gretchen now," Gertrud said, adding, "You mustn't tell her what I told you—she doesn't like me talking so. She's such a dear! But it's been so long since we've had a pastor in the house. . . ."

The door opened and an amazon of a woman stood there. She had on a cotton blouse and a tweed skirt, just like her mother's. Her hair was dark and grayish. Her face was round and masculine-looking.

My first impression proved misleading, for in spite of her size Gretchen proved very warm and genuinely excited over my visit and the sweater. She took her seat at the other end of the sofa and poured herself a cup of tea. She mentioned to her mother that she had to return to the school in the afternoon for another political briefing session. I pricked up my ears and asked what that would be about.

"Oh," she answered, "all the time we have these horrible political briefings where our Utopia is explained to us. Next week we have to take the children down to the Karl Marx Allee again to wave flags for some visiting fireman from Russia or somewhere."

"Have you seen our textbooks?" she went on. I shook my head, so she grabbed a colorful children's book from the shelf. The title was "With Us in the City." She paged through it until she found the story she was looking for and then handed it to me, saying, "Here, read this, it ought to interest you."

I was looking at a short, page-long story printed in the bold type of a first-grade reader. Above the story was the picture of a little Negro boy with blue pants and a red shirt crouching on a piece of grass. I read the story.

**MY NAME IS JACK**

I am a little American Negro boy and I have seven brothers and sisters. Our father is a poor farmer. In the stall behind our house we have an old horse and a starved-looking cow. The land that we have, mother has to take care of alone. She plows and plants the corn in the earth. Mother even harvests alone.

We children would love to help our mother. However, when we are six years old we have to get up at four in the morning to go with Father in the cotton fields. They belong to the white landlord. My brothers and sisters pick almost as much cotton as the grown men, yet they earn very little for their labor. Tired, we come home in the evening at nine o'clock. We would be overjoyed if we could go to school. However, here the government doesn't build schools for poor Negro children.

Because of this our parents are collecting money for a school. It is a simple small wooden building. Little Negro children only go to school for short periods. I trade places with my sister. One of us must always go cotton-picking.

The rich children have it much better. They ride in buses to their big beautiful schools.

Often they make fun of us and no one says anything to them.

Once a white worker from Russia told us about the Soviet Union. There the children go to beautiful bright schools.

In the summer the children go to the sea or to the mountains. They may go hiking or play together. I wish that I lived in that land. Some day, my father tells me, also American children will live happily and be able to go to school.

I looked up, astonished by the crudeness of the story. I began to page through the book. There was a cute drawing of a little girl holding a vegetable with a face on it. The story was entitled: "Vegetable Harvest in the School Garden." Only with a second look did I notice the blue Young Pioneer kerchief around the neck of the girl. Another story was called: "Soon Youth Consecration Time Comes." I glanced through a story entitled: "Dimitri Saves Two German Children." It was the story of how a Russian tank driver saved two children from a house just before the retreating Hitler soldiers destroyed it. A picture of a boy talking with Lenin stood above the story: "Over There Lives Lenin." All of this was tucked in between the usual run of German fairy tales. I set the book down on the coffee table and looked up, unbelieving. Gretchen spoke as she reached for a cookie.

"Oh, don't worry, the children see through it. Just the other day a little first grader asked me why I didn't tell them what I really believe. One of the teachers in one of the upper grades caught a little girl writing a little 'LL' in the corner of all her political essays. When asked what the 'LL' meant, the girl blushed and said, 'Lots of Lies.'

"The horrible thing about it is that the children grow up learning to lie. At home they all watch Western television and at school they all write political essays. Recently in one of the higher school graduation examinations one of the essay questions was: 'The use of weapons is justified if they are used for a just cause.'

"Oh, yes!" she continued, getting up from the sofa. "I must show you the song that we had to teach the children a few years ago."

I read the lines:

"Go home, Yankee, go home,
Split for peace your atom,
Leave alone our Father Rhine,
Do not touch his daughterlein,
Go home, Yankee, go home."

Gretchen laughed. "Oh, that song was really too much. None of the teachers really taught it except some fanatics. After all, we can exercise a little influence—thank God for small favors."

Gretchen sat down again and went on seriously:

"Actually, if it weren't for the poor teachers and the political trash, to say nothing of the lack of funds for equipment and buildings, our education would be better than in West Germany. Over there the children still have to decide between the fourth and fifth grades whether or not they go on to the higher schools or finish out their eight years in the Volksschool. Here we all go together for ten years before the children have to decide for the upper schools or not.

"And as for the poor teachers, most of those political appointments that immediately followed the war have been weeded out now, and we are getting some good and dedicated young people.

Only this horrible propaganda remains the unsurmountable Wall."

"Gretchen," the mother said, leaning forward in her chair and talking in a low whisper. "Don't talk so loud—remember the walls have ears."

"Oh, Mother," Gretchen replied, a little annoyed.

I thanked the ladies for the tea and began to excuse myself. Both of the women followed me to the door, thanking me over and over again for my visit.

The stairs of the old apartment building creaked as I walked down to head back toward the Wall and my home in West Berlin. I was heading toward the Wall, but I felt that many more formidable walls were behind me. Certainly the attitude of my hostess of this morning cut her off from much of the life in her city. Gertrud and Gretchen also have their private walls, their homemade ghetto. The TV and the magazines built walls. So did the textbooks and the schools. In fact, when you look at it, the Wall of stone and mortar built on August 13, 1961, is only one of many walls in Berlin. The other walls are made of propaganda, fantasy, and prejudice. Many of these walls were started long before August 13, and I wouldn't be surprised if most of them will be standing long after the ugly visible Wall which now seems so massive has crumbled to dust. That's why I told you this story of Gertrud, Gretchen, and their friend in West Berlin who had been my hostess in the morning.

You see, most of us foreigners know only the ugly cement-block Wall. We've all seen pictures of it. If we have been to Berlin as tourists we have taken pictures of it. Many have stood silent before the crosses which mark the places where someone has lost his life trying to get over the Wall. Some have even bent off a little piece of barbed wire as a bizarre souvenir. This wall has made a somber impression on the mind of the West.

But look at my hostess of the morning again. She lives in the past. She romanticizes the past. The past has been good to her. She has had a home, a husband, and a national heritage that she is proud of. But something has gone wrong; today she is just another pensioner in a new Berlin in a new Germany. In this new world she has defended herself by building her own private wall. It contains the past and keeps out the present. It is a romantic wall. It probably is also a tragic wall. But it is a real wall.

Old Gertrud in East Berlin also has her private wall. It is also a mental wall. It not only keeps out any good there might be in the present, but it also keeps in all the hurts of the past. It is a high wall—as high as the frustration and desperation of its builder. It is cemented every day by isolation, stories of friends, and unquestioning devotion to Western television.

These explainable little mental walls—these common frustrations and prejudices—are reinforced and used by the professional propagandists of the two opposing German states. West Germany does not recognize East Germany as a state and refers to it exclusively as the "Zone"—"the Russian Occupation Zone." East Germany peppers its occasional references to West Germany with loaded adjectives like: warmongering, exploitive, or revengeful.

These official propaganda lines laid out the blueprint. The foundation was laid accordingly with political acts such as the currency reform, the blockade, the creation of the Federal Republic of Germany, the creation of the German Democratic Republic, the North Atlantic Treaty Organization, and the Warsaw Pact.

Long before the first stone of the Wall of cement was laid on August 13, 1961, a hundred other almost equally insurmountable barriers had been built. A small group of Germans both inside and outside of the church saw these walls of propaganda, fantasy, and prejudice going up and tried to stop the construction. Yet West German critics of developments in West Germany—both in politics and in the church—were easily ignored or eliminated by being labeled red, while in the East all political criticism was automatically labeled Western-reactionary. People in East and West Germany who struggle to try to see both the good and the bad—and these in proper proportion—are more frustrated by these little mental walls than by the Wall itself. The blocks that build these little barricades are the barriers that they bump into daily. They seldom if ever see the real Wall.

The schoolteacher Gretchen sees the advantage of the East German school system in its basic educational philosophy. She believes the prewar educational philosophy which has been restored in Eastern Germany. She believes in the basic outlook, but she suffers daily with the prejudiced and propagandistic texts and curriculum. All day in the school Gretchen tries to soft-pedal the texts to be objective. Yet when Gretchen comes home to her mother she is faced with the opposite side of the coin. Gertrud, Gretchen's mother, refuses to hear anything good about the East or any criticism of the West.

We foreigners stand before the crude reality of the Wall in Berlin and stare in unbelieving shocked silence. We are shocked by the Wall, but the idea of other walls escapes us. We simply don't understand people like Gretchen and her counterpart in West Germany when they try to tell us that the Wall isn't that important and that we shouldn't give it so much attention. We are inclined to dismiss their statements as some sort of unconscious yielding to the stream of Communist propaganda. Sometimes we pity those who seem to overlook the Wall and try to turn our attention to other issues.

We don't understand them, and they don't understand us; this too is a wall. In fact, when you look at it, the Wall of stone and mortar built on August 13, 1961, is only one of the many walls in Berlin. Many of these other walls were started long before 1961, and I wouldn't be surprised if most of them will not be standing long after the ugly visible Wall that now seems so massive has crumbled to dust.

# THE BERLIN WALL

## *The Human East German Question*

*The Deputy* is a play which became something of a sensation when it opened in Berlin in the early sixties. It was written by Rolf Hochhuth, a sensitive young German who seriously asked himself and his generation what they would have done if they had found themselves under Hitler's iron hand. This is an agonizing question, but it is also a legitimate and necessary one. As Hochhuth studied the documents which spelled out the story of the struggle of the Roman Catholic Church with Hitler, he not only discovered individuals whom he was compelled to admire, he also discovered those whom he felt forced to judge. In uncovering the records of those who pleaded with the hierarchy of the church to deal more sternly with Hitler, he also discovered those whose ears seemed deaf to these pleas. He could not admire those who risked everything to try to protect Jews without at the same time judging those who seemed to risk so little or to say or do nothing at all. Just as his admiration found its symbol in the records of the life of a young priest his judgment also found its symbol in the person of Pope Pius XII. He poured out the conclusion of study in *The Deputy,* a play which contrasted the radical and total resistance of a young priest with the studied reserve of the vicar of Christ on earth—the Pope. The play hit the German public like a bombshell because it not only forced the younger generation to question their political responsibility for the events of today but also because it forced the older generation to question anew their actions in the past.

Bishop Otto Dibelius of Berlin attacked the play, saying at one point: "That is a cheap manner of writing history." The reaction is understandable. Bishop Dibelius had been forced to face hard decisions in the war years. Those decisions which he and others had faced were not decisions which were reached in the cool objectivity of detached study. They were decisions made in battle, decisions reached in the tortured and terror-filled hours of nights when no one knew what morning would bring. They were decisions of life and death. They were deeply personal decisions. Only one who had lived through such hours—only one who had personally experienced such choices—could even begin to understand why such decisions were made. This is why the Bishop felt compelled to make the judgment that Hochhuth's play was a cheap way to write history.

The Bishop's protest is understandable, but Hochhuth's question is still legitimate. In the face of today's torn Germany we cannot have any understanding without asking ourselves what we would, could, or should do if we were East Germans. Yet such a question can be called cheap because we are not East Germans. That is why I have included the following story. I did not write this story. I only transcribed it. The setting is dated, but the issues are not. The story is told to you and me by an East German, who found himself and his family on vacation in West Germany on Sunday the 13th of August, 1961, as the wall was built.

* * * * *

We were still at the breakfast table when Mother burst through the door.

"Thank God you're here," she exclaimed. "They've sealed off Berlin. We just heard it on the news. Yesterday the number of refugees climbed to 12,000—12,000 in one day. So in the middle of the night—five o'clock—they start stretching barbed wire. Factory militia groups are standing guard. Big cement blocks are being set up in a wall."

The room exploded and dissolved into a chaos of voices. The children, Inge and Gernod, Helga and Wolfgang, all asked questions at once. My wife Lilo sat ashen.

"I just knew they would do it some day," Mother continued.

I took my bread firmly in the hand, cut it, and spread it. My mind was flooded with confused thoughts: So now they've sealed off Berlin. First the long rusty barbed wires and the dead man's zone from the North Sea, through the center of Germany, to the Czechoslovakian border. Now fresh wires through Berlin. First the border between East and West Germany, now the border between East and West Berlin. This day will go down in history. Sunday, August 13, 1961. Great God, what a day! My home, my homeland—East Germany—The German Democratic Republic—the so-called Eastern Zone or Russian Zone—a national concentration camp—population 17 million internees.

"They almost trapped you," Mother went on. "What if you'd taken your vacation in June as you'd planned?"

It was odd that we should be on vacation in West Germany now. We had planned to take our vacation in June during the Pentecost holidays, but then Basinger (a colleague at our little Protestant Publishing House in East Germany) had gotten sick. The boss asked if we could go later. All during the days that we had planned on for our vacation I sat at the desk reading manuscripts and proofs. Every one of those days had been warm and beautiful and I had then often sat back and stared out the window—stroking my goatee, which balanced off my balding top—and begrudged Basinger his illness.

"You're going to stay—aren't you?" Mother blurted out at me.

I hadn't thought of that before. I mean I hadn't thought that we had an option. When we finally got the visa to visit relatives in Western Germany we just naturally assumed that the visit would be just that—a visit. We weren't fleeing. We came here on a visit.

The courthouse clerk at home had smiled when he handed me the papers. "Sure gonna miss you," he had commented, with an understanding and confiding wink, "but I don't blame you." I remember how I looked at him in puzzled amazement. Amazement that he had spoken so openly. Then I became angry. Why does everyone assume that anyone going west is going for good? How does he get that way, presuming to know my plans and wanting in on my confidences? What right does he have to be so familiar? I calmed down, smiled back, and replied quite deliberately: "No, we'll be back." Then I had picked up my visa and left. Mother broke in again: "You're staying, aren't you?" she asked simply. I answered just as simply: "I don't know—let me think."

It wasn't that we hadn't thought of leaving. Everybody thought of it. We were like the rest. We lived physically in the East but mentally in the West. Our home was in Potsdam, but half the time our heart was in Heidelberg. The only radio we listened to came from West Berlin, and when we watched TV it was never on the East German channels. I was old enough—in my late thirties—to be about as well established as anyone could be in my field in the German Democratic Republic. Yet Lilo and I were young enough to be able to take our four children and start over again in the West. Sure, we had thought of leaving. But it's not so easy.

My wife's mother lives in East Germany. She had been born and reared there in Gruenweide. Even in her old age she still looked young like my wife, not exactly pretty but tall, slender, blonde, blue-eyed. She knows every cobblestone of the road between the farm houses that make up the village. Her husband, her father, and her mother are all in the churchyard there. My wife was born in the room that she lives in. For better and worse, in thick and thin, through two wars as the armies came and went she has planted and harvested in the village. Can she say goodbye to Gruenweide? To old Schenker, the baker, to Auntie Klara, her neighbor for forty years, to Schwester Anna the deaconess? Should she leave them for a new world with us? Could we leave her?

Just pick up and leave. That's all people here think we have to do. Come over to freedom. What is one more gone out of 17 million? Somebody else left behind will take care of the halt, the lame, and the blind. Dr. Pohl did just that. He left in the middle of the day. The office was full of patients. They thought he had an emergency call. Karl, the shoemaker, got the postcard from him a few weeks later informing us, through some not too difficult to decipher greetings, that he was now starting a new practice in a comfortable West German village. We never wrote to him. Why should we? Should we have told him of the misery his absence caused his colleagues, to say nothing of the sick? Should we begrudge him his comfort in the West? Does all that have anything to do with the Hippocratic oath?

"You are going to stay?" Mother asked again deliberately. The room grew silent. The sun shone through the clean modern kitchen of Mother's new apartment. The children were watching me.

"I don't know," I repeated again. "Let us return thanks."

Then turning to the family I reminded them that they would all have to help if we were to get to church on time. They all bowed their heads and I returned thanks, ending the meal.

* * * * *

The little white Evangelical or Protestant church is new in the small West German town that my mother has called home since the end of the war. The town nestles in a winding river valley enclosed between rolling forested hills. In the old days this town was solidly Roman Catholic. Parts of the Catholic church, located in the center of town on the market square, date back to the 12th century. The square and the church are surrounded by narrow curved streets that once, centuries ago, were contained within a village wall. The steep-roofed houses in the old town jut out and up at various angles as they follow the contours of the streets, alleys, and pathways. Mother's new church is out beyond the old town in the section known as the "New Settlement." Here the architecture is that of neat modern three-story apartments, each with balconies, each with flowers.

Here most of the refugees live. The clipped dialect of these newcomers separates them from the old-timers. It also separates Protestant from Catholic. Most of these new people are Protestants from East Prussia, or Pomerania. In 1945 these German provinces, along with Silesia, were placed under Polish or Russian administration, and the Poles and Russians immediately proceeded to drive the Germans out, all nine million people. One still hears horrible stories of the forced flight.

Some of the congregation gathered at the church still show physical reminders of that winter trek. Maria contracted a disease along the way; the fever damaged her brain, and now she will remain a little child as long as she lives.

Johannes walks swaying because of the toes that froze and were amputated. Yet this morning on the way to church together the horror of that terrible march is overcome. The trees around the church are heavy with fruit, the gardens full of flowers, and the worshipers full of satisfaction with their new life. There are even a couple of cars in front of the church. This is West Germany all right! I wonder if the day will ever come when we see cars in front of the churches in East Germany.

That older couple over there looks familiar. Who is it that has that full beard and black cane? Oh, I remember, I thought, as my lips spoke out a greeting.

"Good morning, Herr and Frau Meyer."

. . . . . . . . . . . . . . . .

"Yes, it is a beautiful day."

. . . . . . . . . . . . . . . .

"I agree, the news is shocking, yet in a way expected."

. . . . . . . . . . . . . . . .

"Yes, we are very glad to be here."

The conversation ended as we entered the church. It was full. The bells began to ring. What a funny feeling to see a full church, a church so new and so clean. I sat still, drinking in the warmth and joy that flooded the white sanctuary with the sunlight from the large windows. The altar stood out boldly in the middle of the far end of the building. It was hung with a single woolen cloth colored green for the Trinity season. A simple oaken cross rose behind the altar on the back wall. As the bells stopped ringing the organ began the prelude.

I wonder if Pastor Schmidt back home misses us this morning. Of course he does. You can't take a family of six out of our little East German congregation without having everybody notice it. If you are gone for a joyous reason they all rejoice with you, and if you are gone for serious reasons they all carry you in their prayers.

I wonder if this pastor here in this full and beautiful church can tell when somebody isn't here. Does anybody in the congregation notice? Somebody must. The Lord must pick out somebody among so many who notices and cares.

The hymn. Look at my little Inge. She doesn't know what to do with so many people singing!

It is good to be here. God knows, these people have suffered. They deserve this. Yet we in East Germany suffered too. And we Germans caused our share of suffering all across the map of Europe. Then that is only all the more reason to join in the confession of sins, saying, "Not by our hand but instead from thy hand do we have these things." From thy hand we have these things—well, at least from thy hand *they* have these things. We don't have half as much. Our little church was new before the war but now it looks ancient. The roof has been repaired but the walls are still rain-streaked from the roofless war days. The organ squeaks. The bells were melted down for bullets in '42. So much needs repairing. Why should one half of Germany suffer and the other half receive double blessings? Why, God? I'm sorry.

"Kyrie eleison, Christie eleison, Kyrie eleison."

"Lord have mercy, Christ have mercy, Lord have mercy."

Don't I owe it to my children to let them grow up here? How could I answer Inge when she asked me why we never had oranges at home and Grandma Peters here always has oranges, and bananas? Is life an orange? For Inge perhaps.

I could see the question in Wolfgang's eyes when he saw the new school. After all, he will go into the eighth grade next year. Here there are sunny classrooms, new equipment, and most of all no Young Pioneers—that is, no political youth organization with all its tom-tom, blue shirts with neck scarves, drills, marches, and bands, crude Marxist creeds to be learned, required "voluntary" political meetings and rallies that often called for Sunday morning so that you have to miss church. Back home last month the older Communist youth organization, the German Free Youth, invited the younger ones, the Young Pioneers, to join them in a mass rally in Leipzig. "Of course we will all want to go!" Wolfgang's leader had asked, not really allowing any choice in the matter, so the next Sunday Wolfgang was off on a bus for Leipzig. He didn't want to go, but he felt he had to.

Here in the West Wolfgang could grow up with a choice. He could even choose not to belong to anything and it still wouldn't affect his education or vocation. Here no one really seems to care whether or not you are involved, and knowing Wolfgang as I do, he would probably choose to stay uninvolved. Here freedom is also the license to be irresponsible. What is better then—compulsory involvement or irresponsible noninvolvement?

Yet at home not everything is as forced as they sometimes imagine. We proved that with Gernod when he was under such pressure to join the Young Pioneers at the beginning of school last fall. I pointed out to the teacher that membership was voluntary and that my son was staying out to prove that it was voluntary. I remember how shocked Gernod's teacher was when I took at face value the statement that membership in the Young Pioneers was voluntary. We stood face to face there on the shadow side of the old school in front of the unpainted doors on the morning that I brought Gernod to school. With my goatee and spreading middle, dressed in an unmatched sportcoat and baggy pants, I looked for all the world like a Communist party official. She in her uniform of a leader of the Young Pioneers (to say nothing of her trim figure) looked like a propaganda poster of a belle of the new era. I asked her simply, in a rather pontifical demanding official voice, if voluntary means compulsory! She just nodded her head and sputtered, "Of course not." I cut her off with a short, "Thank you. Goodbye," and turned and walked away with the same pontifical manner that I had spoken. I almost died laughing inside.

More people at home would be freer if they could only free themselves of their fear. They're afraid to ask, or to apply, or to test anything! It's so much easier to believe the worst about others, so all the time they box their fantasies and complain because their life is so miserable. How many people are sitting at home today bemoaning the fact that they are not now in the West? Yet they could have gotten a visa just as we did if they had only tried. Sure, some got turned down, but just as many were accepted. I know of scores of people who are legally in the West this morning. Here in Western Germany when something doesn't go right in the bureaucracy the bureaucrats are to blame. "Damn Bureaucrats," everybody screams. At home when something doesn't succeed it's a Communist plot. Sometimes people are crazy. Nothing to fear but fear itself. Let's face it: there are East Germans and there are East Germans, just like some people here are in church and others are hiking to the Blue Peak.

The organ swelled with the hymn before the sermon and the Pastor left the altar and slowly climbed the broad oaken steps to the pulpit, which exploded out of the east wall of the church like some modern wood and brass trumpet of the Word. The congregation rose with the ending of the hymn.

"Grace be unto you, and peace, from God the Father, and from the Lord Jesus Christ, Amen," the Pastor intoned from his place on high.

His voice filled the church as he read the text and prayed. He grasped the pulpit dramatically as the congregation settled down for the sermon with much creaking of new benches. He held his tense pose and waited until everything was still. Then he began.

> This morning a deep shadow is cast across the face of this land that we call our own. In the darkness of this last night another knife has been drawn through the heart of Deutschland. The entire free world stands this morning, horrified by the dazzle of new barbed wire stretched out through Berlin in the August sun! The sermon this morning should be a call to battle or perhaps to repentance, but in either case the urgency of this hour does not allow us to overlook this deed. . . .

As sentence followed upon sentence a pattern became clear. Using the parable of the Pharisee and the Publican as a text, the pastor was trying to point out the hidden Phariseeism in the West and the hidden good in the East. It was a good point, but still it made me feel uneasy. Talking of the West his voice became strong:

> . . . the Pharisees stand among us and all too easily call across the wire: Extortioners, unjust, adulterers! . . .

Speaking of the East his voice became modulated and mournful:

> . . . Humbled by the division of their homeland, given over to a life under an atheistic police state, forced to pay sevenfold for the sins of their fathers, our eastern brothers . . . .

Right and wrong, true and false. How is the layman to put his finger on it? It sounds great and it makes me sick. It says what I often think and still represents what I despise! Aren't there Pharisees and Publicans on *both* sides of the border? Someone is trying to make this whole thing too simple. We are supposed to be atheists and here everything is supposed to be Christian—the schools, the government, the ruling political party, the Army, the NATO atomic warheads. Couldn't it be that there are some atheists in the West German government—even if they do go to church? Couldn't it be that there are some Christians in our government—even if they don't go to church? Is the opposite of an atheistic police state necessarily a Christian state police? Here a churchman signs a treaty in the name of God to establish a military chaplaincy. Does that mean that if we had chaplains in our atheistic East German army it would be Christian, our cause just, our killing legitimate? Can there ever be anything such as a Christian army, or a Christian land, or a Christian political party? Of course not. God is as much with our soldiers as he is with their soldiers. Nor is it possible for our government to exclude him any more than it is possible for their government to include him. The difference between the Pharisee and the Publican is not a geographical border. There are Pharisees and Publicans, Christians and atheists, good people and bad people in every land.

The pastor was making this same point, only differently. He grasped the front of the pulpit with both his hands and pulled himself down until his face almost touched his manuscript. His face was tense. His voice loud and clear. His hands left the pulpit and moved upward and outward as he declared:

"God is today mightily present in the East Zone. He is present with each East German brother in strength to resist and power to hold out. He is there in pity and solace, in compassion and mercy."

He stood there dramatically in his black robe with his arms extended until the echo of his words died out.

I couldn't help thinking that he had missed the whole point of the parable of the Pharisee and the Publican. How does he get that way, saying God is with us East Germans in pity and solace, as if our situation was so pathetic? As if his new church and large congregation were evidence of God's presence with him not in pity but in power, not in tenderness but in triumph. I fear his outspread arms resemble tragically those of the Pharisee who meant well but still prayed: "I thank thee, God, that I am not like other men." Where would this new church be if it weren't for the government-collected church dues or taxes? We've had the government-collected taxes taken away and our offerings have swollen even though the congregations have dwindled. How big would this congregation be if it weren't still the thing to do to go to church? We've had our religious classes kicked out of the schools. Sure, it's been rough, but we've found ways to teach, and more than that, we've learned a lot while doing it. We know why we are teaching and what the alternative is. Sure, our churches are old and worn, but it's not the building that counts, it's the power of the reconciliation of Christ at work among us. We've learned what that means. We've found our mission and that's what makes us. And that is the power of God at work among us—not pity and solace, but power.

As we sang the hymn following the sermon the minister moved slowly down the oaken stairs to return to the altar. With the end of the hymn the benches gave off their corporate groans as the congregation rose for the closing prayers.

The Pastor began: "O most merciful Father, we lift before you today our brothers and sisters now completely cut off from us behind barbed wire . . . . "

I couldn't hear any more words. I didn't want to hear any more words. I was violently arguing with his prayer. That man doesn't want us to be human. He doesn't want Christ to be enough for us. He doesn't want us to rejoice or to be thankful without oranges, or a warm bath, or a new apartment. He wants martyrs. He wants Good Friday Christians. No Easter for East Germany. No Easter without oranges!

The bells were ringing again as the congregation poured out into the sunlight. I felt terribly alone in the crowd.

* * * * *

The sun was high and hot as we wound our way homeward. The streets were filled. Mass had evidently let out earlier. The windows of the cafes in the old town were open, and one could hear the cordial banter of good friends drinking their after-the-service glass of wine. Many of the young people had already changed and were on their way to their afternoon recreation, some to the soccer match, some to the pool. On the corner a group of the motorcycle-owning elite stood watching the parade of people. Occasionally a cycle would roar down the street or a car would bounce along loaded with Grandpa, Grandma, perhaps an Auntie or so, often a dog or a cat, naturally all the children, and the ingredients for a picnic on some nearby high grassy slope. Some of the younger couples stood studying the shop windows and plotting their finances. With the older couples the men usually stopped for a short one after church while the women hurried on to prepare for the family. Our children went along the street like magnets attracted to every display window. As soon as we would pull them away from one, they would rush ahead and fix themselves just as securely to the next center of attraction.

We all collected in front of the hardware store. The model train in the window went round and round, and eight little eyes followed it in awe. Once before, at the Trade Fair in Leipzig, they had seen a similar one. My wife and I didn't see the train. We spoke no words. A tightening grasp on my arm communicated all that we needed to say. Behind the train stood rows and rows of toy soldiers. Above them rose shelves of jeeps, armored cars, tanks, guns, and imitation uniforms.

At home Auntie Gertrud had seen a similar display when she had come to visit us. She had said: "Isn't it shocking? They're even teaching your little ones to prepare for war." Then she had turned to us compassionately and said, "Oh, I do feel for you brave people living here." That was a year ago. What should one think? Now we were standing in West Germany, looking at the same display of soldiers, and everyone took it for granted. These soldiers belong. These soldiers have American-cut uniforms. Our toy soldiers look Russian. These toy soldiers are "Freedom" soldiers. Ours are Russian soldiers. That was the way Auntie Gertrud had seen it. That's the way most people see it. Yet that isn't the way it is.

I remember when my neighbor boy, Fritz, came home from "boot camp." That was back home. He had become a member of the People's Army. "O God, how I hate it," he had spit out. "Every day lectures and drills. Lectures on a way of life that no one believes in, not even those talking, and drills for a war that no one wants to fight, not even those drilling us. Lies, lies, lies. Propaganda from morning till night. You can't find ten fanatics in a hundred. Everyone knows what the score is."

After a short pause, he had questioned, "Why don't they put us on border detail? Because they know we'd all disappear—over the wire—to the West—to freedom. No, they always send us out two by two with a new buddy every day, so we never get to know each other well enough to make the dash."

We had stood there silently on that day and listened to our frustrated soldier friend of the ironically named People's Army. He had paced back and forth fingering things in our room. When we refused to break the silence he had finally concluded:

"Why can't we just make the best out of this mess we've got? We're willing to work! It's home, isn't it? Okay, leave it at that. We don't want to go West. Don't they understand that? Just leave it at that. But don't make us sign that this is the kingdom of God. . . . I hope we never have to fight."

Fritz was typical of the East German soldiers that we knew.

Jurgend was the opposite of Fritz, in all ways. Jurgend was a West German soldier. We had met him here on our first visit. His family lived in the same building as Mother. After graduating from the higher school he sought every possible means of avoiding the army. Those were great days for him. He belonged to West Germany's educational elite. He padded around in sandals and long sweaters making aloof comments on the relativity of all things temporal. Naturally he hated "boot camp" when they finally drafted him, but by his first Christmas in uniform he had begun to change. Mother had mentioned that she had run into him at the Christmas Eve candlelight service. She had commented on how different he looked in his handsome uniform. We met him later in Berlin—West Berlin. He had been converted. Our conversation had consisted of a battery of questions begun with the words: "Is it true that? . . . " Our answers invariably began with: "Yes, but . . . ." But we never managed to finish our sentences.

"Is it true that Christian young people cannot enter the University?" "Yes, that does happen in some cases but in just as many other cases it doesn't seem to make any difference."

"Is it true that people are sometimes beaten?" "Well, yes, I suppose that we would have to admit that we also have our share of what you in the West call extreme cases. But the old horror of the Stalinist days has definitely ended."

"Is it true that they force Communist propaganda on the kids in the school?" "Well, again the answer is yes. Our government naturally teaches the way of life that it believes in just as in the West the children are taught a largely uncritical view of democracy. But our children are perceptive and they see right through their civic classes. In fact, with the contrast between creeds and deeds so obvious, we often feel that we can argue that our children come out more politically sensitive than yours!"

So our conversation had continued for almost two hours.

His mind worked like a computer. He systematically collected the "Yeses" that we fed him but he just as mechanically rejected all the qualifications that we made. Slowly his mind completed the picture of horror that he had set out to discover. We increasingly said less and less as the hopelessness became more obvious. My insides had churned on that afternoon. I remember that I thought that maybe silence was the only way out. I self-righteously thought, After all, didn't Christ finally shut up in front of Pilate? He did, but I couldn't. I had exploded. I had poured out the picture of the German Democratic Republic that we knew. Not a land of Communists, soldiers, police, party thugs, and propaganda, but a land filled with people. Babies crying, children at play, men and women at work, old people resting. A land of people. Our people. People little concerned with politics but greatly involved with life. Births, deaths, baptisms, weddings.

I still remember vividly leaning across the table and verbally whipping Jurgend with my sentences.

"The sun still shines in the German Democratic Republic. Flowers still bloom in the German Democratic Republic. Couples still laugh in the GDR. Couples still marry in the GDR. Wine is still drunk even if it does come from Rumania instead of the Mosel Valley. Food still tastes good after a hard day's work even if there isn't the variety. The lives of people still count even if they are in the German Democratic Republic."

My defense was followed by a silent pause during which I noticed that a number of tables around us had been listening. Jurgend broke the silence by leaning over toward me with a confiding smile and whispering:

"You know, old friend, I detect that some of that propaganda is even beginning to rub off on you." That was the last time that we had seen Jurgend.

Wolfgang and Gernod were still glued to the window watching the train. If we decide today to go home then some day these boys of ours will probably become soldiers of the People's Army, frustrated like Fritz. If we stay here they may become fanatics like Jurgend. What can we do? How can we decide?

* * * * *

Sunday afternoon in Germany consists of a walk. The procession starts slowly, shortly after mealtime, and swells during the high afternoon hours as more and more people finish their dishes and more and more children wake up from their naps to allow their parents to join others in getting some fresh air. Round-bellied older men meander slowly, periodically emitting dark clouds of heavy cigar smoke and faintly resembling tugboats chugging upstream. Older women are more graceful as they move along with their interests from house to house, from flower garden to flower garden. The children dart in and out and back and forth in little schools that are sometimes on trikes and bikes but more often on foot. Occasionally a car of some sort will pick its way politely through the people. In West Germany the population has made a truce with progress. As more and more cars flood the roads the Sunday walkers have more or less conceded the main roads to the traffic. In fact, some walkers even enjoy going down to the highway to watch the motorized parade. There are two-wheelers, three-wheelers, and four-wheelers from little Volkswagen bugs to big chauffered limousines. The side roads remain the property of the walkers and the pushed and pedaled vehicles. The villages and towns are concentrates of people. Europe does not have the land to expand. Apartment houses are the rule, as are little gardens with vegetables and flowers. The transition from town to country is often abrupt.

One wonders what the difference is between East and West Germany. It is the same Germany, and yet it isn't. The transistor radios carried by the young people are only slightly more modern looking than those at home. The music is the same. Our young people listen exclusively to Western stations, as I have said. The clothes are perhaps a little more colorful. The flowers are the same. Naturally. Perhaps it is only the new plaster of new buildings that sets them off more dramatically. The cars make the obvious difference; the children want to go watch them. And the streets don't smell of cheap gasoline. Yes, the smell is different! And the signs. Everywhere there are colorful little signs advertising this or that. On the sides of buildings. On fences. Now and then on posts. On the side of the road up ahead there is a large crucifix freshly repaired and painted with a little garden beneath it. Right next to it there is a large enamel placard announcing that the house behind the crucifix is the "Greentree Inn" serving Dortmunder Beer. One wonders when the old Catholics tip their hats as they stroll by whether they are greeting God or the Dortmunder Beer.

Mother's little town of five thousand has twenty-eight such "inns." In German they are called Guest Houses or "Gasthäuser." Now that's a difference. At home we have only a dozen in a town half again as big. Ours are usually larger but grayer. Somehow it seems that even our bright colors never reach that gleam that one finds here. All right, I'll admit it. Western paint is better. The crowds are the same, though. After all, for generations the Gasthaus has been the terminus of the traditional Sunday walk. For those who can afford it the Gasthaus is where one eats the dessert and coffee of the Sunday meal. Ironically, more people can afford it in East Germany than in West Germany. At home there is much less to spend money on. Everything is in short supply. You have to wait two years for a car even if you can afford it. That's half the reason. The other half is the fact that you are more likely to find something tasty at the Gasthaus than in the store. At home we know when a particular Gasthaus is allowed a ration of whipped cream for their Sunday afternoon pies; then all the heavy old ladies of the Whipped Cream Brigade gather around the tables there to have a few delicious bites of nostalgia for the good old days of the Kaiser.

Maybe that's it. At home we still have the past—in a way. The present is alien—Russian—Communist. Somehow no one in East Germany has really fallen in love with the utopian New Jerusalem promised by the Communist propaganda. It is different in Poland and Russia. The Poles and Russians have never had it so good. For that matter, most of the people of eastern Europe have never had it so good. Sure, the rich had it better in the old days, but they were few and far between. The masses have never had it so good. It doesn't do any good to argue with them how much better they might have had it. They didn't get what they might have gotten but what they got was better than what they had.

This relative prosperity isn't so in East Germany. We have seen better days. Somehow when we think of better things we think back through the mess of two wars and pick out those golden memories that aren't too mixed up with the guilt that we carry. Those of us who have any roots at all romanticize the German humanistic tradition. In fact, even at formal functions in the East the new people's rulers follow protocol patterns more reminiscent of the court than is the business-world-influenced informality of the West. You'll look long and hard to find a Western headwaiter in coat and tails, but that is still standard at any of our better restaurants. Maybe the reason is that when our leaders look ahead they look forward to a life for the masses that is equal to what the rich had before. Anyway, much of the past is still with us because that is all we have. Consumer goods, gadgets, modernization, mechanization, all of these haven't caught up with us. At Christmas the traditional celebrations still dominate the days because there is not so much to crowd them out. The celebrations are all that we have.

In a way East Germany is still the Germany of the Weimar Republic or even the Germany of Kaiser Wilhelm II. That's a strange thought. East Germany is still on the threshold of her future. West Germany has plunged in. West Germany has married the West. Maybe the worst of the West. Here in West Germany they even sell Coca-Cola. The French call that Coca-Colonialism.

West Germany has chosen America. She loves America. "A chicken in every pot and a car in every garage." That's the dream. That's the goal.

Look at everyone sitting around us here in the Greentree Inn. People who have made it. Is this what we want? That's the question so many of us easterners ask. Is this the way we want to go? Is this what we Germans want our new Germany to look like? Are we just being defensive when we feel that something is being lost or smothered here in the West? There is more money here and that buys more things and there are more things to buy and that makes life easier and that should be good. It should be, but is it?

Mother is looking at me with every bite of her pie and with every look she is asking: Are you going to stay? She won't ask out loud again. She'll just keep looking and waiting.

Lilo is looking at her children—our children. She is wrestling too. We'll talk again tonight.

Helga is playing with her ice cream. She's tired. She's seen me looking at her. She's speaking. "When are we going home, Daddy?"

"Right now, darling, as soon as I pay our check."

My mouth formed the words that called the waitress to the table while my eyes answered Helga's real question. "Daddy doesn't know yet, darling. Mommy and Daddy still have to think. We don't know yet."

* * * * *

It was that hot nervous hour of the late afternoon when the big Mercedes with the Goettingen license pulled up in front of Mother's building. The children were on their way to bed and Mother was in the kitchen cleaning up after them and preparing the cheese, coldcuts, bread, and beer for our last meal of the day. I had taken advantage of my Sunday noninvolvement to light up another western cigar and I almost fell asleep smoking it. It was so quiet and cool in the lengthening evening shadows. The bell rang. I heard Mother open the kitchen door and move through the hallway to the glass door which separated the hallway of her apartment from the hallway of the building. In the next moment the door to the living room opened, Mother switched on the light, and there stood Rudolf Vanderheim. Even on this hot day he was dressed in a conservative business suit with what was for me a surprisingly narrow tie.

"Oscar." His hand shot out as he came across the room. I was on my feet.

"Rudolf, for heaven's sake, what brings you here? How did you know we were here, and to what do I owe the honor of such a visit?" I was now thrilled with excitement. We in East Germany always love a visit. Our lives just aren't as crowded as in the West—at least with such things as pleasant surprise visits from close professional colleagues. Rudolf and I had known each other in the old days when we worked together as book pages in the largest book store in Berlin. After the war Rudolf had found his job waiting for him in Goettingen and I had returned to my proof reading desk in a small church-related publishing house and book concern. At least once a year we saw each other when the Circle of Protestant Bookdealers held their annual meeting.

For the last few years these meetings had always been held in Berlin—at considerable financial disadvantage to many in West Germany—so that all of us from the East could join in. These yearly gatherings had long since lost the formality of professional gatherings. For us the yearly meeting was the event of the year. To be in Berlin meant to be free. We would walk blisters on our feet shopping in full and stylish stores and shops. We would look our eyes half blind at the full-shelved and uncensored bookstores. And then (delight of delights) we would join our friends to discuss all the gossip and news of the trade in some fine restaurant with a menu full of almost forgotten delicacies. In the late evening or dim early dawn hours our western friends would spirit us back to our East Berlin hotels in their cars. Only one of our eastern group had a car. Yes, just yesterday a West German could drive through the Brandenburg gate with only the wave of his identification card and be in East Berlin. Just yesterday any East German could walk across the border between East and West Berlin with only a short show of his papers. Only yesterday. Now it would no longer be possible.

Rudolf was busy filling me in on the news events of the day. A number of people had stormed through the wire. At Brandenburg gate a massive West Berlin crowd had gathered, and the East Germans had moved up water spray trucks. When he had heard this news he had thought of his many friends in the East, and then he had remembered a recent letter from a mutual friend of ours which had told him that I had gotten my visa to visit my mother here with her family.

"It couldn't have worked out better!" He said as he ended his long explanation of his presence.

My wife came into the room and froze in her tracks. She evidently didn't know Rudolf was here. Then she exploded into greeting. It was obvious—almost too obvious—that a familiar face was most welcome on this day of tension. Mother came into the room after Lilo and began to set the table. Soon linen covered the usual woolen tablecloth, the plates were set, the sandwiches brought out, and we were invited to the table.

"Bless, O Lord, this food to us and us to thy service, Amen."

As I raised my eyes Rudolf spoke:

"I'm prepared to offer you the same job that you had in the East with our firm here in the West, and at a salary equal to your talents and our quality."

A lightning glance passed between my wife and me and then we both looked at Mother who in excited joy—much too obvious joy—was watching Rudolf.

"We have no intention of staying here," I said to Rudolf in a sentence that was half a statement and half a question as to why he thought we might take the job.

Mother fastened her eyes on me. There was an awkward pause.

"I know," answered Rudolf slowly, concentrating on our conversation, "that it will be a hard decision for you, but there is only one way that you can decide."

His voice was intense, "I sincerely hope that the knowledge of a good position will ease the pain of readjustment."

I didn't answer. Rudolf continued deliberately.

"Before today you always had a choice. An either/or. Up until last night you could either stay in East Germany or you could escape through West Berlin. Now that is no longer possible. The German Democratic Republic is making progress. The Stalinist days are gone. There is a semblance of rule by law. Food supplies have been worse even though the collectivization of last year didn't help matters. The situation of the church is tolerable. There are only a handful of names on the list of those in prison for religious reasons, and you and I know that even some of these cases are questionable. We realize that the economic recovery of East Germany is almost more remarkable than that in Western Germany when you consider that the Russians didn't help you at all. No, they robbed you while the

Yanks helped us. All of these facts are comforting. All of these facts help you carry the difference that exists between East and West."

"But Oscar, you also know that that is only one side of the story. You remember that schoolbook that you showed me when we last saw each other. The lies, the slant, the distortion was appalling, and that book is still being used in the schools that your children will be going to. The pressure to join the Young Pioneers is there even if Gernod hasn't joined yet. You yourself told me of the fanatical teacher who came into the classroom and greeted the children as "Young Pioneers and Gernod." Next year Wolfgang will face the pressure to go to the Government's Youth Consecration ceremony instead of being confirmed. You know what he will learn there in the preparation classes that have replaced the confirmation classes. And if Wolfgang should choose to go to confirmation instead of Youth Consecration you know the psychological price that he will pay. And your wife."

I was getting nervous. Rudolf continued.

"You are one of the lucky ones. You have a little house—but the roof leaks, the sills are rotting, the plumbing is almost primitive, the chimney is dangerous, the place is almost impossible to heat, and there are no supplies to do any fixing even if you had time or money to afford them."

"Your office still has work to do. You are still getting a decent enough ration of paper to print with. You still manage to get enough readable stuff through the censors. You still have a job, but you also know that the government wouldn't give a tinker's dam if your publishing house went out of business. You know that at best the future holds only the same daily struggle for life or an even harder struggle. Realistically speaking, there is no hope for improvement. You are a proud and good mate on a sinking ship. You want to do your job and you are doing a great job, but no matter what you do you know as well as I that the ship is sinking—slowly but surely."

Rudolf didn't say another word on this subject for the remainder of the evening. He was that sort of friend. He had made his case, and he had enough compassion to shut up after that. We turned to discuss the business here in the West and the welfare of his family, then slowly drifted to small talk, which consumed the rest of the evening. I fear that the wonderful cordiality of that evening with a good friend and good wine argued more eloquently with me than had any of Rudolf's words. It was so much like the warmth of home.

It was late when Rudolf left, and soon thereafter Mother excused herself and went to bed. Lilo and I were left alone. She brought some fresh sandwiches from the kitchen and as she reentered the room her eyes were twinkling. She stated politely:

"I think we should send Karl the shoemaker the postcard of the new church."

The irony in her voice surprised me. She was tense, and her speech and actions were dramatic as if she were mocking someone.

She continued, "I thought we could write: Dear Karl: Greetings from Neuheim—which of course means "New Home"—isn't that obviously subtle?"

"Then we could write: 'How is Hans doing with his bicycle?' Which would inform him that we meant for Hans Stolper to have Wolfgang's bike. 'Does Ursula like her roller?' would tell him that Ursula should have Helga's scooter. Then we could end with something like: 'We do hope you all are fine—we miss you so much—we wish you were here!"

She spoke her sentences with exaggerated accents of sincerity. She was acting.

"Lilo!" I said severely.

"You know," she went on, ignoring me, "I've been thinking all day what will happen when the police come to confiscate our home. I didn't tell you that the other day our local store got in their half-year allotment of toilet paper and while I had the chance I bought 20 rolls. Just think what will happen when the police open up the closet and discover 20 rolls. A hygienic gold mine! But will they appreciate our hygiene? No! The big man in the green uniform will look around at the other men—knowing full well that their wives would buy just as much if they could—and then he will pronounce in his most Marxist voice: 'You see these people are capitalist hoarders!' "

She laughed at her little joke and then slapped her hand over her mouth imitating a small child that had just said the wrong thing. Her tense smile was still visible behind her hand as she went on.

"Oh, I'm sorry. I forgot, we East Germans aren't supposed to laugh. Be sober, Lilo. If you don't look like you're carrying a cross people won't know you're Christian."

"Lilo," I reprimanded.

"Wouldn't they die," she continued, "if they could hear us telling jokes on Walter Ulbricht at home."

She struck a pose of a party official and asked herself a question.

"Lady! Walter Ulbricht, the First Secretary of the Party and the leader of the East German people, has just died. As a representative of the people, where do you think it would be appropriate to bury him?"

She changed her pose to that of a cleaning woman and answered her own question.

"Any place but in Jerusalem. One feller already comed back to life down there once."

"Lilo," I said, half to myself.

"Here, Inge," she continued parodying Inge's Grandmother, "here's an orange, and after supper you may have a banana before you go to bed."

"That's not fair," I said to her quietly but firmly, but it was now too late to shut off the releasing flow of the day's stored-up emotion.

"My dear husband," she continued, "do have some more Mosel wine. It will do your spirits good. It isn't the best in our cellar, but then it's better than that Rumanian stuff you are used to."

"Lilo," I said again, but she continued, her face drawn, her eyes on the verge of tears.

"We can send Grandma fresh fruit every week. A box full of oranges full of vitamins, won't she love that? And in the winter warm woolen sweaters and coats. We'll send her lots of pictures to show old Schenker, and Auntie Klara, and Schwester Anna. She'll say: 'Look, Anna, this is my Wolfgang. You remember when he was here last year before they cut off Berlin. Well, just look; now he's been confirmed! They sent me his picture by special delivery—it only took six days!' "

"Lilo, please," I said quietly.

She stood silent. She didn't hear me. She was mentally embracing her mother, reassuring her. She was greeting old Schenker and the rest. She was back home.

Then in an instant she was here again and still fighting.

"What difference does another 6 make among 17 million? Somebody else can fight your little books through the censors for the firm. After all, it's a sinking ship. Oh, I know. Rudy meant it well. Somebody else can help and the others make the best of it. It doesn't have to be us. Somebody else can question the teachers, test the laws, bring out what is good in the bad. Somebody else can do it."

She was breaking. The irony of her words was cutting her. I reached for her.

"Somebody else will be glad for the house. The congregation will get over our absence. After all, they still have God. God is still there. God is still left in poor old East Germany."

She quit.

We just sat there. The windows stood wide open and in the distance we could hear an occasional car down on the highway that wound through the old town. The evening breeze stirred the curtains as it entered the room. Lilo sat back, tired, in her chair. Her face was still drawn. Her eyes tense. As we spoke to each other in the silence her face relaxed. We never uttered a word as we reached our decision.

# THE STRUGGLE FOR REALITY

"But it isn't like that! It isn't like that!"

These are the tragic words that so often pour out after an initial East-West contact. They are words of frustration. They often come from both sides. Why?

First of all, there is the obvious frustration of the language barrier. But in reality this is very minor. Much more important is the frustration arising from the communication which does take place. To put it simply, we talk about the wrong things, ask the wrong questions. We get hung up on the wrong issues. This is, in fact, the real source of much of the frustration in so many East-West encounters.

Actually it is easy to see how this happens if we stop long enough to look at what really takes place. We tend to come to Eastern Europe with a newspaper-headline knowledge of the countries. We know East Germany is Communist. It has a Wall. It's hard to get into. It's impossible for its citizens to get out of. These facts, and perhaps a few others, are more or less the limit and extent of our knowledge about the land. Obviously this knowledge is limited. Obviously this knowledge is selective. Naturally with such a background we are bound to ask certain obvious questions. We ask about the Wall. We ask about Communism. In other words, we tend to ask about the big social and political issues that we know about. We tend to ask our questions. What we usually don't realize is that this trend of conversation is actually very frustrating to an East German host. His frustration only slowly becomes obvious to us when the table is turned and he begins to ask us questions. He asks us about the war. He asks about race relations. In fact, even though it is already old history to us, he will probably ask about Kennedy's assassination. Many an American has stood tongue-tied and dumbfounded somewhere behind the Iron Curtain as question after question about such momentous issues has been thrown at him.

The unreality of such an encounter is obvious. The American visitor wants to protest that America is more than the race riots and street murders one reads of in the headlines. The East German wants to protest that life in his land doesn't begin with a breakfast discussion of the Wall and end with a supper discussion of Communism. Both parties are frustrated because all the time the wrong questions tend to be asked. But that is only half the problem. The situation is compounded by the simple fact that poor questions tend to elicit equally poor answers. Again the fact is obvious that most of us know very little about big issues like race relations or the national economy. Therefore when we are questioned on such subjects we tend to answer with our opinions. When asked about Kennedy's death we dismiss it with the few sentences that sum up our opinion on the subject. The same goes for our answers to other "global questions." The result is often unfortunately a collection of not too informed opinion about selected headline issues from both East and West. It is this result that almost inevitably leads to the comments of frustration from both sides after such an initial engagement.

Both sides end up saying, "But life isn't like that!" The American really wants to tell about the little things that actually fill up his days: his home, his family, his garden, his vacations, the man he works with, the church he goes to. What the American really wants to say is that these things are the center of his life and that the other big social problems actually only occasionally touch him. This is also exactly what the East German wants to say about his life and land. In fact, what both parties really want to say is that the important questions are not the questions that we ask each other but instead the questions that our daily life brings us. The important problems are the day-to-night struggles that fill our working hours and not the momentous social upheavals which continue to happen regardless of what we say, do, or think about them. These daily challenges are the questions which must be understood before we can attempt any understanding or evaluation of a person or a land or a way of life. Communism is not the big issue in East Germany, not directly at least. Neither is the Wall. Most people there have never seen it and seldom, if ever, talk about it. What absorbs their existence is the daily struggle with the gray world around them.

When we go to East Germany we have to try to understand this world, its pressure, its problems, its joys and sorrows. We have to listen for questions that life there is asking instead of looking for reactions to the questions we bring with us. It's as simple as this: We need not the right questions but rather the ready antenna.

# BLACK SATURDAY

*or Life in the German Democratic Republic*

The rain stopped in mid-afternoon as I arrived in downtown East Berlin. The sky was still dark and the streets were wet as I entered the big old office building. The single bulb hanging from the ceiling cast an eerie light in the staircase, and the hallway was cold and clammy. I opened the big iron fire door and entered the offices of the little firm where my friend worked.

I could hear typewriters clicking behind the various partitions that divided the office space. I became excited at the prospect of surprising Walter. I opened the door but his office was empty. I walked into the grayness and turned on the light. I sat down in the empty office. A big wooden desk stood at an angle in one corner of the room. It was piled with papers. On the wall there was a bulletin board with the picture of a stained glass window on it. I recognized it as the Christmas card of a common West German friend. Other corners of the board were covered with a few post cards and little poems salvaged from the newspaper or magazines. One pathetic plant stood on the window sill with a blanket behind it to cut off the drafts from the old window. The long single bulb lamp with a green shade hung so that it came right above the corner of the desk, giving the desk enough light without forcing it to be set straight in the room. At this end of the long room there was a table covered with an old woolen cloth. A clothes rack stood behind the door. Books lined one wall and in among the books were a kettle and two battered cups. The telephone was old, with the receiver supported by two high hooks. A dirty scatter rug covered the floor.

This was the difference in the GDR. The eternal grayness. The change was the changelessness. Everything the same. The same tall sweating windows year after year. The same wooden desk. The same green-shaded single bulb lamp. If you paint the room, the green shade still miscolors the painted walls. Besides, paint doesn't cover the bumps. Every week you have to wipe the spots around the window-sill where the draft blasts the dust in. You wipe it clean and the wall gets streaked. Your rag gets dirty. The bucket gets dirty. The water gets dirty. Even the soap is dirty. Everything is twenty or thirty years old at least. If you want to paint, you have to wait and watch like a kingfisher until you hear that there is some paint in some store, and then you dive for it, hoping you aren't too late. You emerge from the store triumphant with the paint, and you see someone else turn away disappointed. You ask yourself whether you need the paint as badly as the disappointed one. You picture a young couple bringing home their first baby to a dingy unpainted crib room. Still, you got there first.

You want to fix the windows. You nail strips of cloth on the frames to cut the drafts, but they weather and tear and you have scraps of rags hanging from the windows. You break a window and you replace it with a board and decorate the board with a colorful doodle because there is no glass right now. You invite your colleagues in during coffee break to see the artistic panel that you have improvised. Everybody drinks coffee and ohs and ahs about the panel, but when they leave it still looks like a board patch on a broken window.

Your life is one eternal patch. Clothes are made over and reissued, but the children still recognize them. You get tired of patching. Life is a squirrel cage of torn clothes, broken pipes, empty shelves, worn wires, broken ropes, tired people, and crying children. Nobody knows the word "surplus"—evening after evening is spent improvising, searching, or bartering.

The windfalls are few and far between and when a shop suddenly gets a surprise load of fresh fruit in the long gray days of spring, it is gone within the hour, and then the arguments begin among the neighbors. One mother was washing and didn't hear the news. Another was on the other side of town visiting a sick uncle. Their children cry. Their husbands curse because their children are crying. They promise their children an orange some day if they will only shut up. No, they don't know when, but some day. Resentment breeds. Hatred is sown. The stovepipe falls. There's no wire. Go see if you can find some wire. Do you know of a shop in town with stove pipe? No stove pipe in town because when stove pipes came into the stores everybody bought some to hoard it, so now half the people have a reserve and you can't get a replacement. You tremble. You seethe inside. You wrap the pipe in an improvised metal casement and know that when you get home from work tomorrow you have that job waiting for you.

You sit down in front of the television and see West Berlin. Fruit on the table. You get angry again. Cars on the street. You resent West Berlin. You hate East Germany. You resign yourself and go into the bedroom that you share with two of your children because of the shortage of housing. You take off your patched clothes and try to sleep.

I was still sitting there alone, half in the light and half in the shade of the single bulb when Walter could be heard coming down the hall. His footsteps drew near.

"Who's in my room?" his voice boomed as he threw open the door. "Prince Otto von Bismarck!" he said, rearing back and smiling at me. "Oh, I know you're not, but it would be so much more interesting to pretend that Otto Bismarck was here instead of just another old American from West Berlin. Improvisation is the genius of life in the GDR," he continued dramatically. He shut the door and moved across the room to deposit some bags on his desk before taking off his coat.

"There," he said, straightening out his tall muscular frame and twisting his mustache up. "I'll be the Kaiser and you be Otto von Bismarck."

Striding back across the room to hang up his coat, he bowed to shake hands and said: "Very glad to welcome you, Prince von Bismarck." Then he hung up his coat and exploded into laughter, saying, "Oh, how wonderful that you should come on this horribly depressing day.

"Come, we shall have a feast," he continued. "Look, I have some grapes! All of a sudden in the middle of March a carload of grapes comes in from Bulgaria. One of the girls noticed them when she went for a walk during the noon hour, so we've all been down there this afternoon standing in line."

He held the grapes up high above his head and in pantomime he created a Bacchus figure.

"Just a minute," he said, breaking the pose and grabbing the tea kettle as he strode across the room and out the door. I have often wondered how this man keeps up his eternal exuberance. Day in and day out, rain or snow, no matter what may befall him, he has a smile and an encouraging word. He returned to the room and sat down across the table from me.

"Perhaps you would like a—using the term loosely—cigarette?" he asked, pulling a blue package of Eastern "cigarettes" from his pocket. This was a familiar move on his part. I usually saw to it that I brought a couple of packs of Western cigarettes with me. You can bring up to fifty single cigarettes with you legally. This morning I had forgotten. I had only the remains of my package. I offered him one. We lit up.

One of the young girls in the office came into the room with a little teapot in one hand and a bundle of papers in the other.

"Here is your tea," she said, "and here are the reports that have to be in today."

"As for the tea, I thank you, my dear," Walter answered, "but as for the reports, if I finished them today they would lie on the boss's desk for a week, and then they would go to the license bureau, and then they would be around another six months waiting for various permits and authorizations from his majesty's government, and if we were lucky the project would get under way in two years. So what difference does another 24 hours make? Can't you see I'm having tea with Prince Otto von Bismarck?"

The girl gave him a hard look that was half annoyance and half amusement. He didn't give her time to protest but made a gesture with his hand and commanded, "Away with you, woman, away, away!" He sat down again and poured the tea.

"Wouldn't you like to come out for dinner?" he asked. "We're having asparagus. Don't ask me why! I hate the stuff, but when little Ule went to the store this morning to get the can of milk he saw that they had gotten in a load of asparagus. So off my wife goes and buys asparagus! She hates it. I hate it. The kids hate it. But because it's a luxury that our store has once or twice a year, we feel obligated to buy it, and tonight we will all sit down to eat it and say, 'Isn't this delicious asparagus?' as we almost gag.

"Most husbands and children in the world rush home from work and school to see what Mommy has cooked for them, but not in the GDR. Here the women rush to the store in the morning to see what the Government Central Planning Commission has given them to cook with today, and the husbands and children come home to see how mother has fixed the potatoes tonight.

"Tonight we are going to skip grace, and instead we will raise a fork of asparagus and shout three times, 'Heil to Ulbricht!'

Walter leaned heavily on the table and stirred his tea as he spoke.

"Renate is sick. She has a cold. She's running a fever. All we've got is aspirin. I've been tempted to ask you to smuggle some antibiotics over here, but I'm not going to. It's too dangerous. Renate will just have to let the thing run its course like in the old days. At least we have some lemons.

"Ulrich is going away with the Young Pioneers this weekend. My wife is upset about it. She says his teacher is such a fanatic."

Walter's exuberance was visibly waning. It was a frightening thing to see. We had long been on a first name basis, but it was obvious that he was taking me now another circle deeper into his world of reality.

"Old Walter has about had it," he said, emotionless. "Old Walter, the eternal clown."

He looked across the table and smiled weakly, saying: "If you will allow me?

"Have you ever heard tragic stories about clowns? Clowns are often favorite figures in novels and plays. Tragic figures. The mask is that of laughter, but underneath there are often tears. The clown makes believe. He lives in a world where things are as everybody wants them. With the clown the sun is always shining. With the clown the world is right, everything is good. The jester dances before the king and makes a fool of the king. The jester spits venom in the face of the king, and everybody laughs. His jest vicariously relieves everybody. But when the jester goes home at night and takes off the grease paint in front of the mirror, all he sees is the tragic fool who pretends that reality isn't real. The fool who makes everybody feel better but doesn't change a thing."

Walter sat slumped over the table back-lighted by the green-shaded bulb. His mustache seemed to sag on his face. His right hand slowly fingered a small bunch of grapes he had laid out upon the table.

"It's like one eternal Black Saturday," Walter continued slowly with a sigh. "Good Friday with all the pain and the drama of the crucifixion is behind us. The veil of the temple is torn asunder, the earthquake is over, the eclipse is past. It is that limbo of in-between —Black Saturday. No Easter; just Black Saturday."

"You can't talk like that," I said, and I was overwhelmed by my own audacity to pretend to speak like that under these circumstances. Down on the avenue sat my powerful new powder-blue car, and in a few minutes I would drive up to the Wall where only last night a young man was shot down. I would drive up and joke with the guards. I would wait with the other visiting foreigners in the control booth and then I would tramp on the gas and with a wave I would be in West Berlin with the world at my door.

Walter looked up and blew out a deep breath, saying, "I know better, but sometimes asparagus does strange things to people."

# PART TWO

## THE CHURCH IN EAST GERMANY

# EINE ZWISCHENBEMERKUNG

*(which actually means: a little in-between observation)*

It wasn't until 1871 that the Germany we know today actually became a political unity. Up until that date Germany was a hodge-podge of little states and kingdoms, united only occasionally in various political or economic federations.

In the early days of the Reformation the principle *cuius regio eius religio* was applied, which meant that according to the conviction of the ruler of the land, so the religion of the land. As toleration spread, Protestant churches were established in Catholic lands and Catholic churches were established in Protestant lands.

The Protestant Reformation brought two main Protestant streams into Germany. Coming up the Rhine River from Switzerland and cutting through Western Germany was the Reformed influence. In the course of time various Reformed congregations were established in Lutheran regions and Lutheran congregations in Reformed areas. In 1817 King Friedrich Wilhelm III of Prussia united the Reformed and Lutheran congregations in Prussia, and other lands followed suit by creating Union churches. Usually the majority was Lutheran, so that Union actually meant only the absorption of a Reformed minority. This explains the pattern as we have it today, with 13 Union Regional Churches, 13 Lutheran Regional Churches, and only 2 small Reformed Regional Churches.

Although various attempts were made at uniting the Protestant churches, each Protestant territorial or regional church remained autonomous until 1922. Following the first World War and the abdication of the Kaiser and other rulers, Germany became a Republic, but in the *Federation of German Protestant Churches* founded in 1922 the churches united only for common national and world tasks. On the regional level they remained independent.

When Hitler assumed power, an attempt was made by the Nazi government to create a single national Protestant Church, and in 1933 the German Evangelical Church was forced into being. Through control of finances and other methods Hitler managed to dominate the church, or at least to paralyze the regional churches. (Churches in Germany are financed by church dues which are collected by the state along with the other taxes as a special service to the church.)

The exception to Hitler's rule was the Confessing Church. Inside of the various regional churches that were semi-absorbed into Hitler's German Evangelical Church, individual laymen and clergy and sometimes entire congregations began to become concerned about Hitler's German Christian blasphemy. These concerned Christians gathered from all over Germany to form the Confessing Church. In their famous Synod of Barmen (1934) they declared their faith. In the Synod of Dahlem later in the same year they became an independent nationwide disestablished German Protest Church dependent on themselves alone for finances and theological education. Rule in these confessing churches was exercised by councils of the brethren organized on various levels.

Since the Confessing Church became the major rallying place of all ecclesiastics who for whatever reason opposed Hitler, the Confessing Church collected a lot of men during the war who worked along with the Confessing Church but never really accepted the principle of radical disestablishment from the state which the Synod of Dahlem proclaimed. Nor did those who sought only refuge in the Confessing Church ever seriously accept the principle of a Believers' Church instead of a national *Volkskirche* or People's Church. As long as the war went on, the terror of Hitler held the divergent movements within the Confessing Church together. As soon as the war neared its end, men began to jump off the ship of the Confessing Church to begin the work of the restoration of the regional established People's Churches.

Bishop Otto Dibelius tells of his leap with these words:

> A Russian grenade thrower still sat beside my residence in Lichterfelde, as we began the restoration of the structure of the Evangelical Church in our German fatherland.
>
> The immediate problem at first was Berlin.
>
> Here, in Berlin, it wasn't decisions alone that we needed. We needed also wisdom, prudence, and tact. A false step could have unimaginable results. The Russians were just starting to establish a civil government, the civil government of a totalitarian state. If they didn't find everything in the church solid and clear, if, for example, some little opposition group within the church should turn to them for help—and in Berlin everything was possible—then we could expect with certainty that the Russians would set up Church Commissars as they had done all over the East. Then instead of Nazi church rulers we would have Communist ones . . . .
>
> This threat needed to be met. The Russians needed to be confronted with a church in which everything was clear, unobjectionable, uncontested, and with legal foundation. There was only one alternative open—to rebuild on the foundations of the existing legal forms.
>
> Now this naturally was not exactly according to the intention of my young friends in the Confessing Church. They had never experienced what an orderly, solid, and thorough church administration was. For them a consistorium was the epitome of fickleness and senility. It was "Old Church" and they didn't want to have anything to do with anything "Old Church." Their church home had been the councils of brethren in the Confessing Church. It still was. A brotherly council, with neither superiors nor subordinates, that in brotherly unity discussed and decided everything. Such a council must take over. So they had thought. So must it be now.
>
> But that was completely impossible for an ecclesiastical prov-

> ince with 4 million Christians and 1,000 to 1,500 pastors. The Confessing Church had never really learned what the administration of the entire church structure entailed!

By the time the Confessing Church got together in the summer of 1945 after the end of the war in May, most of the Regional Churches had reestablished themselves. The Confessing Church established the fact that Hitler's German Evangelical Church of 1933 was illegal because of its unconstitutional creation. The Confessing Church therefore considered itself the Protestant Church in Germany, built upon the legal foundation of the Synod of Dahlem of the Confessing Church in 1934. It was too late, however. Otto Dibelius arrived at the Treysa Synod of the Confessing Church in August of 1945 as the new Bishop of the Church of Berlin-Brandenburg; before the war there had been only a president of this church. As we have seen above, he felt compelled to restore the pre-Hitler Berlin-Brandenburg Church.

Martin Niemoeller, who had just been released from near-death in a concentration camp, stated the case for the Confessing Church:

> Then certainly in our midst there should be no doubt about the fact, as Herr D. Wurm has already put it, that a restoration of the church built on the conditions before 1933 must under no circumstances take place, if the entire struggle, suffering, and offering of the last twelve years is not to be in vain. We simply cannot go on as if nothing has taken place. We cannot simply take a joyful step forward, for it might well be a step direct into hell. Before we can begin, we must turn around to the right way.

But it was too late. The Confessing Church petered out and remains today as various loosely organized "brethren councils" inside the regional and national churches.

Today the two Germanys have 28 regional churches, of which 13 are Lutheran and 13 are Union. Two small Reformed churches count around a half a million members.

From the 13 Lutheran churches, numbering over 20 million members, ten of the regional Lutheran churches are banded together in the United Evangelical Lutheran Church of Germany. From the 13 Union churches, also numbering over 20 million, six are banded together in the Evangelical Church of the Union. All 28 of the regional churches form a federation which is "The Evangelical Church in Germany." Therefore, Germany today has 28 regional churches with one Lutheran "super-church" and one Union "super-church," all together under the federal Evangelical Church in Germany.

A key to the story of the German church is the postwar struggle between the Restoration and Reform movements. Naturally in West Germany the Restoration thinking of the church found support, and in West Germany most of the old privileges are to be found, such as government collection of church taxes, religion in the schools, and the military chaplaincy. This has led to the restoration of a strong established church in the West. In the East the tendency has been the other way. The state has refused to collect the church taxes for the church, and the Eastern churches have discovered "stewardship." The state still honors some older agreements which provide for some state support. Religion has been excluded from the schools. This has been accompanied by an active atheistic propaganda and by pseudo-religious state ceremonies. This forced disestablishment of the church in the East has naturally assisted the reform elements within the Eastern churches, just as the restoration in the West has hindered the reform elements there.

# BERLIN

There they were—37 members of the First Presbyterian Church of Fertile Valley, Minnesota, in Berlin for 38½ hours to learn all about the church in Communist East Germany. They were on a two-week tour of Europe from Copenhagen to Rome. Last night they had stayed in Hamburg—or was it Hanover, they couldn't remember—but it was one of those cities up there on the map. The day before they had done Denmark. They were exhausted.

This morning they were an hour ahead of time, but then their guide and tour leader, the Reverend Mr. Gover, had decided to use the hour to take them off the main highway and show them the barbed wire border between East and West Germany. They had all taken pictures of the fence that marked the border. They had found a section that was electric, and they all got beautiful snaps of the electric fence with the raked dead-man's strip behind it and with the manned watchtowers in the background. It had made quite an impression. When they got back on the highway they were twenty minutes behind time. Then they came to the control point where they left West Germany to travel 100 miles on the *Autobahn* through East Germany to West Berlin. At the control point they had all been required to get out of the bus and get special travel permits from the East Germans. This had taken hours, so when they finally arrived in West Berlin it was late afternoon and, as I said, they were exhausted.

As they registered at the desk of the little hotel that had been arranged for them I stood by and helped with the translation. It was fun. One lady just couldn't contain her love for Copenhagen. She confided that she had skipped lunch and gone window-shopping and, wouldn't you know it, she had found two of the loveliest candlesticks. The next person in line explained that this trip was to be more than just another tour. This trip had a purpose. They didn't want to be like every other American tourist. They were here to study the religious life of Europe. The next man, Mr. Carson, wanted to know if he could buy some milk somewhere. His ulcer was acting up. I wondered to myself: whose ulcer wouldn't act up after doing Denmark in a day?

I had been waiting for them since early that morning. I had cut my classes at the Free University where I was enrolled in a doctoral program in sociology. I had received a leave of absence from my church in America (I am an ordained Presbyterian minister) to come to Germany in order to study the life of the church in Communist East Germany. I had known the leader of the group, Mr. Gover, back in Minnesota. It was natural for him to write to me when he started organizing this tour to ask whether I would help his group get the picture in Berlin. In fact, that is about all I had been doing this summer.

The challenge this group presented was simple. They knew nothing significant about Berlin. They wanted to know all about Berlin. They had 38½ hours.

Most visitors are like that. They will spend $2,000 or more to get to Berlin for a few hours, but they won't spend a couple of dollars for a little book to introduce them to the city and its problems.

As if this weren't bad enough, Berlin is the worst place in Europe to arrive at cold. Berlin isn't exactly neutral, like Rome or Copenhagen; Berlin is a city cut in two by a horribly visible wall. Berlin is a city still technically under military occupation. Berlin—at least West Berlin—is an island of a different way of life located behind the iron curtain in a Communist land. Berlin is the symbol of the divided Germany. Therefore Berlin is a city where passions are inflamed, prejudices rampant, and no issue is neutral. Every Berliner is a crusader, from the taxi drivers to the city and government offices that spend millions showing visitors their story through lectures, pamphlets, films, books, receptions, and even free tickets to the theater.

Even the church is politely engaged in this favorite Berlin pastime. The Press Bureau of the West Berlin office of the Church of Berlin-Brandenburg hands visitors a moving little booklet praising the restoration in West Berlin and attacking the East with many loaded adjectives and pictures of the Wall. In East Berlin one can easily pick up a little booklet put out by the Eastern Christian Democratic Party—yes, such a party does exist—giving all sorts of rosy examples of church reform in the German Democratic Republic.

For the visit of our friends from Fertile Valley I had a plan.

* * * * *

The next day dawned warm and clear. When I walked into the sun-flooded breakfast room of the little hotel everyone was ready to go. The women had packed their purses to diaper-bag size, and the men were all wrapped up in the leather straps of their photographic equipment. The women's hats looked like the ones Germans wear to masquerade balls. A rendezvous in East Berlin was our goal, but as we headed down the street to the subway we felt and looked more like we were going to a carnival. This was the most wonderfully American-looking group of Americans that I had ever seen in Berlin trying not to look like Americans.

We all got off the subway at Koch Strasse and headed down the street toward the Wall. I stopped at Checkpoint Charlie and registered the group with the American soldiers in the little white hut in the middle of the street. The group got out their cameras and shot away at the Wall. They were quiet now. Some were obviously a little frightened. Before us stood the Wall.

The Wall is not an easy thing to go through, psychologically. Your feet move you across a little white line painted on the street and your mind screams: you are going behind the Iron Curtain. There is about fifty feet of no man's land inhabited only by two East German customs officials who give the incoming cars their first check and two East German border guards who guard the customs officials. Fifty feet behind the line that marks the real border you walk through a narrow passageway in the Wall. For a brief second you have barbed-wire-topped cement on both sides of you. Then you are in a Communist land. You cannot cast off years of subtle anti-Communist conditioning in fifty feet. You are frightened.

We stood in line before the control house. Slowly the line moved in. As long as we were on the outside we watched the customs officials search the cars. It was similar to the glance-over our cars get when we go to Canada or Mexico, but somehow here it seemed worse. Inside the building we all passed our passports through the little window and then later we were called to declare our currency. After the currency declaration the passports disappeared for the last time into the back room and soon all of us had our papers and were ready to go. A couple of girls had been ordered to empty their purses. That ought to teach them not to carry so much. They were scared to death. We walked down the street to the wire fence that surrounded the control area and we were in East Berlin.

Suddenly there was a corporate sigh of relief. Everyone began at once to pour out his or her reaction to the adventure as we moved off down the street.

The Wall was almost the end of the streetcar line. The conductress was visibly delighted to have the Americans invade her car. She studied each of us as we got on: the clothes, the purses, the rings, especially the hats.

The streetcar bounded along parallel to the Wall two blocks away. Most of this area, even though it is the center of Berlin, is still an unrebuilt field of leveled war rubble. In both East and West Berlin there has been a hesitancy to build near to this unnatural border. Then all of a sudden the car goes under an old railroad bridge and the picture changes. Ahead are the beautiful tall enamel apartment buildings of the best rebuilt section of East Berlin. I assure the half-a-dozen questioners that it is all right to take pictures and the cameras start clicking out of all the windows. Now all around us there are people. We are in a large traffic circle surrounded by tall modern buildings.

"Why, I never knew it was like this," the lady next to me commented.

"Why, it's just like Sioux Falls!" she continued, making the unavoidable comparison to "home."

The car jolted forward again. We began to pass through long blocks of gray buildings, each about four stories high. These were the typical store and apartment buildings which made up the heart of all Berlin, only here many of them still showed scars of the war, and now and then the paint was prewar. The storefronts that lined the street level of the buildings were without either exciting displays or attractive signs. There were people enough on the streets, but it was obvious that we were no longer among the prosperous of West Germany.

We emptied out at one corner, and after a walk of a block or so a church building appeared. This would be the first big test. The sight of the building itself was bound to evoke sympathy. Its deserted look was in sharp contrast to the teeming life of the scarred and gray apartment buildings that hemmed it in.

We opened the heavy doors and entered a long, dimly-lit hallway. At first everything looked and smelled dirty. The walls had lost almost all evidence of the paint they had once had. The dark wainscoting looked simply dirty. Yet as we wound up the stairs we discovered that everything was spotlessly scrubbed and polished. In fact, the recognizable odor of the close hallway and stairwell was that of scrubwater and furniture wax. We emerged at the top of the stairs into a large parish-hall-like assembly room. Again there was wainscoting around the room. There were three tall, narrow windows along the street side of the room. They let in a minimum of air and sunlight. The drapes hung motionless and faded. On the wall opposite the windows there were pictures of ecclesiastics of a bygone era. They were proud-looking men in dramatic poses, often bearded and dressed in the black robes with the white neckbands of a German Protestant clergyman. At the long end of the room opposite the door there was a crucifix alone in the middle of the wall. Beneath it stood a piano and a large glass-enclosed bookshelf with many faded volumes.

The stage was perfectly set for the first encounter of the day. The pastor of this church, our host, is typical of about half of the East German clergy. He is one of that dedicated group of men, most of them older, who are very much products of the institution. His life is the church. He is in his element as a politician at the meeting of the consistory, or as a teacher in the religion classes once taught in the schools, or as an ecclesiastic celebrating worship in a full church. In a bygone era he was a big man. This fact is hard to forget. Today there is more than a little pathos evident in his life. He yearns for the past. He dreams of a different future. He is lost between yesterday and tomorrow. He holds the present and all those related to it in contempt. Yet he is proud. At least consciously he doesn't want any pity.

I always start my introductions to the East German church with a visit like this one. It gives the pathetic, persecuted picture that most Americans have either heard of or imagine for themselves. This picture is a necessity. It is the necessary beginning point of basic reference and contrast. Our group took seats at the long table in the center of the room and on the chairs along the wall. I went to tell our host that we had arrived.

Pastor Heinrich Karl Ludwig von Koenigshausen didn't even slow down for the door when he entered the room but sent the door flying open as he burst into the room shouting:

"Velcome! Velcome!" His accent was heavy and guttural. His voice was one of those that at once commanded attention, and the little conversations died right where they were, in the middle of the sentences.

"Oh, I am so glad to see you, my dear brother von America," he said passionately as he instinctively picked the Reverend Mr. Gover out of the group and extended to him the right hand of welcome. Pastor Koenigshausen was a man in his late fifties, neither tall in stature nor slender in girth. He was dressed in a black suit and wore a silk striped tie. His face was round, warm, and full of expression. A few wisps of white hair still clung to his balding head.

"Oh," he exploded again, turning to the group, "it is zo vonderful zhat you all have come."

A funny thing had happened. As the Reverend Mr. Gover rose to his feet to greet Pastor Koenigshausen, the group also instinctively rose. Everyone was standing now. It was a very moving moment for the group. Pastor Koenigshausen invited the Reverend Mr. Gover to join him at the head of the table and then suddenly realizing that everyone was standing he embarrassedly said: "Oh, please be seated—please be seated." The Reverend Mr. Gover had unconsciously sat down with a friend in the group and Pastor von Koenigshausen had also just as unconsciously moved him up to the head of the table where this German pastor knew, according to long years of tradition, he belonged.

The room grew silent. Pastor Koenigshausen rubbed his hands. He was obviously searching for just the right words to start his speech. He found them. He looked up and spoke slowly in a heavy accent.

"I want to sincerely thank each and every one of you that you have taken seriously the command of our common Lord, and during your wonderful tour of Europe, you have been willing to submit yourselves to the humiliation of going through the Wall in order to come here to visit your brothers and sisters in prison."

He paused. Perhaps he was trying to decide whether he should go on with his East-Germany-as-a-prison theme or not. Then his face relaxed into a broad smile and he took the cigar out of his pocket that I had brought for him. I had told him that the Reverend Mr. Gover had picked it up for him.

"Oh, my dear friend," he said, turning to the Reverend Mr. Gover, "I must thank you for this cigar. You know we have cigars but they are horrible! I mean they were horrible, until the time that you Americans gave us Cuba. Now at least in our dismal captive life we have good cigars and pineapples—thanks to your American generosity."

He smiled at his little joke as he puffed to light his cigar.

"Western cigars still taste the best," he concluded.

Now he drew himself up, breathed deeply and began:

"Today I want to tell you three simple little things about East Germany. I want to tell you about a heritage, a tragedy, and a hope."

"First of all our heritage. East Germany is the heartland of the Reformation. Within our borders are the villages of Eisleben and Mansfeld where Martin Luther was born and reared. Here are the cities of Magdeburg and Erfurt where he went to school and university. Here is Wittenberg where the 95 theses were nailed to the Castle Church door on October 31, 1517. Eighty per cent of our 17 million people are Protestant. These are divided into eight regional churches.

"But all of this doesn't tell you anything. The Germany of our heritage was a good Germany. Our family comes from East Prussia near Koenigsberg where Immanuel Kant lived and wrote. It is Russian today. My father studied in Strassburg. It is French today. Those were the days when Bismarck gave our workers sickness insurance, accident insurance, and disablement insurance, the beginning of our socialized medicine and social security that you Americans are still arguing about. And that was in the 1880's.

"The church sat in the court of the Kaiser in those days, and the entire parliament went to prayer. Pastors and bishops were respected guests at important councils. Great charity works arose. Hospitals, railroad missions, old people's homes, missionary societies.

"I remember well Sunday morning in our beautiful churches in

East Prussia. The buildings were old and large and the bells would summon the farmers from miles around. They were a God-fearing people and they would often bring their Russian and Polish farm hands with them to the Holy Service. We brought the richest fruits from the ground that God had given us. We gave the finest care to those unfortunates that lived among us. We gave our children the finest education centered around the Word of God taught by the pastor, and we were regular in our offering up of divine worship.

"This is our heritage."

Now his demeanor changed. His fists were clenched, his face wore a frown, his eyes glared, and his voice boomed.

"This is our heritage, but now a tragedy has befallen us. Today a man who carries the title of professor to the disgrace of that honor writes trash like this:

> "It is naturally clear that our historical materialism and our dialectical materialism are of course also atheist, for every materialism which aims at honesty and consistency must be atheist. . . . We must make it clear to our youth that they must believe in man, in the development of mankind, and in the fact that man can and will comprehend all, and that mankind in its development can create everything that human society really needs. This belief in mankind is what we have to put in the place of the belief in a God. . . .

"The party has moved in. They have taken away the railroad missions, confiscated the hospitals, old people's homes, kindergartens —although they have given some of the more thankless institutions back because they didn't find them so easy to run. They have cut our publishing work to a dribble. They have forced religion out of the schools, and when we tried to hold our classes after school they passed a law that children could not attend any other classes until they had been out of school for two hours. They say that this is so the young people will get some fresh air, but we know that it is to hinder us. The government no longer collects the church taxes for the church, and they give us only a pittance from the endowments that they took away. They can build workers' halls all over the place, but the houses of God still stand in despair and some in ruin.

"As if this were not enough they have not been satisfied with only attacking us, they have gone one step beyond and turned their party into a substitute religion. East Germany is the only place in the Communist bloc where that has happened. Today parents are encouraged to take their children to a so-called 'Namegiving' ceremony held in some party center where the state gives the baby a bankbook with 100 marks in it.

"The worst is the Youth Consecration service which has been introduced to replace confirmation. The young people are required to attend classes for a year and then they go to a big rally where they have all sorts of speeches, and finally the young people take vows to support the country, socialism, and materialism. Then they are given a big book that gives the Communist view of the world. Sort of a Marxist Bible.

"Let me read you the vows that they take at this Youth Consecration service:

> "Are you prepared as true sons and daughters of our Farmers' and Laborers' State to work and fight for a happy life for the whole German people? If so, answer me by saying: Yes, this we pledge.
>
> "Are you prepared to give your all for the noble cause of socialism? If so, answer: Yes, this we pledge.
>
> "Are you prepared to give yourself for friendship between all people and to join the people of the Soviet Union and other peace loving lands of the world to secure and defend this peace? If so, answer: Yes, this we pledge.
>
> "We accept your vows. You have taken your place in the marching millions who are working and battling for socialism. We welcome you into our German Democratic Republic. With united strength—forward!

"When you want to get married you had better get married by the party or else you don't get an apartment. If your loved one dies you had better have him buried by the party or else you don't get your pension.

"That is the tragedy of our days. A tragedy of empty ceremonies, empty churches, and empty lives."

The passion had ebbed in the pastor's voice and he was now just adding a few last strokes to his gray picture of tragedy.

"The theological faculties of the six universities are still supported by the government, but that is only so that they can send in Communist theological professors. Our students still go there but most of them finish off in a sort of semiofficial church-run school. Most of the clergy are loyal."

The cigar in the pastor's hand had gone out and he now took a long pause to light it and stoke it up again. Then he straightened himself up and continued.

"I have told you of our heritage and I have told you of our tragedy. Now let me tell you of our hope. Let me read you a portion of a radio sermon of our Bishop Otto Dibelius:

> "But we still have the hope that other times will return again. God has not yet spoken his last word, and his last word is never judgment but grace. That is that wonderful thing, that Christians have, that they can trust in. Also in my life I know that God's last word will be a word of grace. That lets us go joyfully into each new day that God gives us. That gives us the confidence that God has something great and holy planned for our people. Therefore we dare not be pessimists. Neither dare we be skeptics. We remain God's rejoicing people and look ahead, up, and out of this present valley of God's anger to the future of heavenly grace for the sake of our Lord Christ. And God will not disappoint this confidence."

Pastor Koenigshausen was obviously moved by this passage. He had read the sentence about the confidence that God still has something great and holy planned for his German people with a deliberate emphasis as if he were reciting a creed without which he would perish. These words kept him alive in his valley. He lived with his grand memories and waited patiently for the restoration that he was confident must come. A grand past and a future hope sustained him in the shadow of the present.

"I guess that's just about it," he said, and he smiled, indicating that he was finished.

He stood alone at the end of the long table under the cross, between the piano and the glass bookshelf, and smiled.

The Reverend Mr. Gover got up.

"Thank you so much," he said to Pastor Koenigshausen as he firmly shook his hand.

"This has been an hour that we shall never forget in our entire lives."

"Nor shall I," replied the German pastor.

The group moved out of the room and down the dimly lit stairs to the big oaken doors. The brightness of the sunlight was jolting. The noise of the street made us realize how silent it had been in the church. We moved along the sidewalk. A few stopped to snap a picture of the church, and Pastor Heinrich Karl Ludwig von Koenigshausen stood waving in the crack between the two big oaken doors of the church. We had been a ray of sunshine in his day. We were messengers from a place where things are different. We gave him hope. He needed us. He waved until the last one of us disappeared around the corner.

I congratulated myself. It couldn't have gone better if I had written the script. Now the stage was really set to complete the encounter with the church and the German Democratic Republic.

* * * * *

It was late afternoon when we assembled again. After the visit of the morning we had taken lunch in one of the fashionable "showplace" restaurants on the Karl Marx Allee. The food had been good. After lunch we had split up and gone our several ways. Most of the group had wandered in and out of the shops along the Allee. This area doesn't especially cater to the tourists, so the shopping had consisted mainly of looking at Eastern appliances and materials. These things might have thrilled an East German who hadn't seen a washing machine since before the war, but it was pretty boring for a group of Americans. In fact, the styles coming in in East Berlin looked like the things that went out of style back home before the war.

To say the least, the Fertile Valley Presbyterians were warm, footsore, and tired when we finally arrived at the small church hall where Hans Johann had promised to meet us. It had not been easy to arrange a visit with this young factory-working minister. He was always busy. Days he worked and nights he gave to his ministry. He didn't want to take time out to talk to another group. He had complained to me that there was too much talking.

I didn't even realize he had arrived until I heard a voice saying rather loudly: "Excuse me. I'm late." Hans Johann stood in the doorway. He was a tall, slender young man of perhaps 32 years. He was still dressed in the blue work clothes that marked him and the rest of his colleagues in Europe as factory workers. His black hair was mussed up from his long bicycle ride. His smile flashed. He too was warm and tired.

Before I could even get to him, he said: "I'm glad that you've come. My name is Hans Johann, and if you will give me a few minutes of your time, I'd like to try to give you just a little picture of the other side of life over here."

With that he wrapped his legs around a chair in the middle of the group and sat down. Everyone had just sort of taken seats anywhere they could find them in the disorganized room. I crossed my fingers.

He began:

"We start here in the German Democratic Republic at the very same point from which you start when you are at home in America. Shall we sum it up with the verse: 'God so loved the world that he gave his only begotten Son that whosoever believes on him should not perish but have everlasting life.' "

He paused and looked one of the men directly in the eye and asked: "What is the subject of this sentence?"

There was a long embarrassed pause and then the answer came—"God."

"That's where we begin, too," Hans replied. "We begin with a faith in God. We don't start with a church, or a past, or a future dream, but with the present reality of God. But what kind of God is he? A God who loves. What does he love? The world. Not just the Christian world, not just the Western world, but the world. East and West, American and Russian, rich and poor, black and white, communist and capitalist. And how much does he love the world? So much that he sent his only Son that we may live—not die, not give up, not hold out, not just see it through—but live, live it up. That's where we start. With God with us. With Immanuel. With the incarnation. With God with us here and now in the German Democratic Republic!"

Hans paused, a preacher in factory clothes, straddling his chair.

"Our faith is our first fact. The second fact is a tragedy—the tragedy of a people who didn't remain faithful to the faith, the tragedy of the church."

Hans stopped again, although he had just begun. He was looking for words. Suddenly he smiled a broad, handsome smile and laughed a little to himself as he continued.

"How can I explain to you in ten minutes or even in ten hours the tragedy of our church? And is there any sense to it? Is there any sense to digging up the past?

"Let me say just a few things. There were two Germanys in the old days too. There was the Germany of the rich and the Germany of the poor. The Industrial Revolution hit Germany between 1850 and 1900. This was the time of Bismarck. If you want to know what life was like in the Europe of the Industrial Revolution, read Engels' *The Condition of the Working Class in England.* Open that book to any page and you will find an unbelievable picture of human misery.

"Well, the poor write few books, so there is little history of that division in Germany. The books were written by the professors in the universities, the clerics in the courts, and the gentry with their leisure, and they saw only what they wanted to see."

Hans's voice was becoming strong and he was moving through the room as he spoke.

"Oh, the Germany of our forefathers was a pious Germany. Piety is the heart of our heritage. Daily prayers. School-taught religion. Beautiful churches. Erudite sermons. Charitable institutions. Uncorruptible integrity. Unquestioning obedience. Grace at every meal. Pious to the core. Pious but blind. Blind. Blind to the hungry, thirsty, homeless, naked, sick masses being bred by industrialization.

"The only Germany that the church saw in those days was the Germany they wanted to see. The Germany of pleasant rural villages where the mayor sat in the front pew of the church and the pastor sat in the chair of honor at the meeting of the town council.

"Oh, of course, a few prophets saw what was really happening. Wichern, for example. He founded the Inner Mission. But what happened? It became a chain of charitable institutions. The pious rich gave money to the church to build a hospital to take care of those broken in health because of the working conditions of the factories of the rich—those same pious rich.

"Alms, instead of a hand, were given to the least of these our brothers.

"Four-wheel Christianity—that's what we had. The pastor and the mayor cracked the whip, and they wheeled the babies in the prams to be baptized because that was the German thing—excuse me, the Christian thing to do. Another crack of the whip of social pressure and the young people went to confirmation classes for a year and were wheeled again to the church—this time in some richer relative's carriage or car—to be confirmed. The next time, they arrived at God's house in the white wedding coach with four white horses. Naturally they were married in the church! And at long last they wheeled you back to the church again in the black wagon of the funeral parade. Four times in your life. Four-wheel . . . Christianity?"

Strong gusts of wind began to blow outside and it grew very dark. The wind was cool and the curtains billowed into the room. Hans continued:

"In 1874 a survey showed that 80 per cent of the weddings in Berlin were justice-of-the-peace affairs and 40% of the kids weren't baptized.

"Where were the masses?" They were with another movement. A movement that promised meat in the soup of the day instead of pie in the sky when you die by and by. The factories and pubs were the churches of this new hope, and Marx was the prophet."

Hans paused. He was tense. He was frustrated. He knew what the reaction would be to what he was about to say and he didn't know whether to risk his whole presentation by going on, yet what he wanted to say was his conviction. He said it.

"I consider myself a Marxist."

"Can't you understand," Hans went on, arguing with an imagined resistance, "that I could never identify myself with the church and the Germany that I have just described? I am prejudiced. Just as prejudiced as those pompous churchmen who think the past was all golden. Look at the past. Bismarck and the clergy blind to the workers. The Kaiser. Armies marching to the first war with weapons blessed by the church and with belt buckles that said, *Gott mit uns* —God with us. The church suddenly saying that politics was none of its business. The hell of the war. The failure—in an ocean of blood and horror—of the old Germany. The tragedy—the utter horrible tragedy.

"Is it any wonder that we disillusioned of this generation are so fascinated by Marx, that crochety old firebrand, who first saw—or at least so clearly saw—the contradictions of the old order? For all his economic theory he was still driven by one thing: a compassion for the condition of the poor and an Old Testament prophet's indignation against the exploiting rich."

Hans still stood, with his arms hanging and his palms turned out.

"Irony of ironies. Karl Marx—that old Jew—becomes the symbol of Christ's compassion."

With that he sat down. He went on, more quietly but still deliberately.

"So that's the faith and that's the tragedy.

"Where are we now? We're right here! We're sitting here in East Berlin, the capital of the German Democratic Republic, talking to a group of Americans, trying to help them understand how a faith in Christ compels us to accept much of what Karl Marx wrote, reject much of what the church says, and live each day with the portion that the Lord gives us, no matter whether we are in the East or in the West.

"What I mean is that we feel that our call as Christians is to seek the welfare of the city wherein the Lord has set us, if I may quote Jeremiah. We happen to be in the German Democratic Republic. We have our particular problems. West Germans have theirs. Our task is to be a little Christ to our brothers and our neighbors, to quote Luther this time. So here I am a factory worker. Sure it's hell. But then, didn't Christ descend into hell?

"We go to hell because that's where the people are. The people are not in the church praying: they're out in the world living. If the church is heaven and the world is hell, then it's easy to see who won the game.

"We don't go and start new kindergartens, but we do our best to see that the kindergartens that the state runs are manned by concerned girls—Christian or not. Then we do our best to see that they are supported.

"For the most part we have given up going to church. The services are dull, the ministers pompous, the sermons defensive, the fellowship cold. Instead we gather once a week for hymns and Bible study.

Really there are house churches scattered all over East Berlin. On Sunday we join the excursions. Work as a youth leader—even with a big bad Communist group—if need be.

"We don't go around trying to undermine everything the government does, but we seek to help things get better. We keep the Marxists in line by quoting Marx at them, just as we long ago learned that the best way to help the church was to preach Christ to it.

"We say a big 'Yes' to the German Democratic Republic and then a lot of little 'Noes.' We say a 'No' to the Army. We say a 'No' to atheism. We say a 'No' to police or party pressure if it shows up. We say a lot of little 'Noes' but we preface them with our big 'Yes' to the GDR. It is because we accept the GDR and say 'Yes' to it that we can say 'No' to the things that blight it.

"The common attitude is to say a big 'No' to the GDR. Most people prefer—even here—to still call it the Soviet Zone. They say 'No' to the GDR as a state, but 'Yes' when it comes to service, 'Yes' to GDR postage, 'Yes' to GDR garbage collection, and so on."

Mr. Carson was perched right on the edge of his chair and when he noticed that Mr. Johann had more or less come to the end, he jumped right in with a question:

"What can we do to help?"

Hans Johann studied him for a minute and then asked: "What do you mean?"

"Well, I mean—" Carson began to reply haltingly, "I mean I feel you're a Christian. I don't understand about being a Marxist, but I know an honest man when I see one. I want to help. Your life isn't easy here. We've seen quite a bit today. How can we help you? What can we send you? Do you need money? . . . "

Hans interrupted the question before it was fully stated.

"No, no, you don't understand. We don't need your help. Well, I mean that we don't need it in the way that you want to give it. We don't need pity. We don't need sympathy. We don't need dollars or food or books or things like that. We get along all right. We are a poor land, but we are not that poor. We have enough to get along on, so you shouldn't feel sorry for us just because we aren't as rich as you are. We are still better off than most of the world.

"No, if you want to help, don't help us but help Christ. Help Christ not here in East Germany—that is our mission field—but you go and help Christ in your land. Please excuse me when I say this."

Hans turned on all the personality that he had and spoke directly and compassionately to Mr. Carson.

"We haven't had a church or home burned or bombed here in a decade. We haven't had any shootings or murders here for a decade. We haven't heard of beatings or harassment around here for a long time now, but we've heard of all of this going on in America!

"Yet we are supposed to be a police state and you are supposed to be a free democracy. Frankly, I feel safer in East Germany than I would feel as a Negro in the American South. Don't ask me what you can do for me. Ask Christ what he wants you to do."

The room was dead silent. Yet it was a live silence. A long, live silence.

Finally Hans went on:

"Excuse me. Please excuse me, but don't you see that that is what Christianity is. At least that is what I feel it is. The ability to talk to each other and to carry each other in prayer, not as the rich carrying the poor or the blessed carrying the stricken, but as brother helping brother. I guess I am just a little sensitive on that helping bit because of the West Germans always coming over here wanting to help their poor brothers out."

There was another silence. Everybody was on the edge of his chair ready to speak, but no one spoke.

"Thank you all," Hans concluded, "and the Lord bless you on your travel and in your mission. I must go now."

Now everyone spoke. People began to get up.

Hans left the room, shaking a few hands, and by the time I got outside he was halfway down the street on his bicycle. I found Mr.

Carson standing next to me. He looked at me and said simply, "Whew."

* * * * *

Thirty-seven of the 38½ hours allotted for Berlin were already gone when I met the group again in West Berlin the following morning. In fact, they had packed the bus and checked out of the hotel before they headed for this last visit. As I arrived they stood in the patio-like front courtyard of one of West Berlin's modern churches. As I approached they were arguing whether the church looked more like a gas station, a movie house, a restaurant, or a modern art gallery. A deaconess came out of the five-sided red door; as she walked toward us she was reflected in tens of windows located at different angles in the structure. She was a heavy-set woman with round red cheeks and puffs of white hair escaping from her starched white cap. She wore the long-skirted dark blue garb with hideous black shoes barely visible. She looked as old-fashioned as the church was modern.

The cameras snapped as she explained to us that she would show us the church, after which we were invited for a second breakfast. She apologized for the pastor of the church, who would join us later.

The sanctuary was a completely new adventure in architecture for all of us. It was a sharp contrast to the dingy buildings we had seen in East Berlin yesterday. Here the congregation sat at various levels and at various angles surrounding the altar with the pulpit behind it. The room was flooded with light, but no direct light could be seen. Various sections of the ceiling were of different colors, and the baptismal font was a brass bowl set in a garden of sea-worn pebbles and stones with plants growing here and there.

"How many people will the church hold?" Mr. Carson asked the deaconess.

"We have room for three hundred," was the answer.

"And how many members does the parish have?" Mr. Carson continued.

"Thirty-eight thousand!" came the answer.

This stopped the entire group, and time was taken to explain that while practically everybody officially belongs to the church, most of the people don't attend services. In fact, it was only because of the church-levied and government-collected dues from such a large parish that this structure could be financed.

A second deaconess appeared and asked us to the coffee room.

Upstairs the tables were set with clean white linen and a third deaconess was busy pouring coffee. The group was visibly delighted with the hospitality.

"How many usually come on Sunday?" Mr. Carson continued.

"Oh," the deaconess replied, "we usually are quite full—I'd say 200 to 250."

Mr. Carson just sat there with his plaid jacket, sport shirt, and two camera straps. He wore a frown. I was watching him when I noticed the church's pastor, Reverend Geiger, enter. He was a tall man, built large. His face was reddish. He was dressed in black with a white silk tie. He introduced himself to the group and began talking as if this was a breakfast table chat.

"First of all, let me welcome you to our little church and to West Berlin. We are always happy to have visitors and we are especially happy to welcome American brothers and sisters. Why, in only the last week we have had three different groups of your countrymen!"

That statement was a *faux pas*. You never tell a group that thinks it is doing what nobody else does that they are the fourth group in a week to do the same thing.

"The other groups," the superintendent continued, "had a little more time to see West Berlin, and we were glad to show them around. We maintain, you know, that Berlin is worth a trip.

"Your guide, however," he continued, giving me a nod, "has done the right thing. He has elected to take you to East Berlin. It has been most gracious of you to go over there and visit our poor brothers and sisters, and although I know that it must have been a very strenuous day I am sure that it was the right thing to do."

The pastor was standing right next to Mr. Carson, and in the split second that he paused between sentences Mr. Carson spoke up as if it were only a private table conversation and asked:

"Why do you call them poor brothers and sisters?"

The pastor froze and turned on a forced nervous smile. Something of yesterday had rubbed off on Carlton M. Carson; quite unconsciously he had thrown the pastor a real curve-ball. In the tension of Berlin a question like that is loaded.

"Why do you ask?" the pastor replied, now quickly recovering his balance and just as swiftly getting his defenses up.

For Mr. Carson this was just like a mid-morning coffee break down at the Corner Cafe in Fertile Valley, so he answered quite leisurely:

"Well, it all depends on how you define rich and poor, I guess. If you look at the shops and so forth, then the people over there are pretty poor. I mean, the buildings are only half rebuilt, and where they are rebuilt there isn't much to put in them.

"But that young man we met yesterday. He told us he didn't like it when people called him poor. I've been thinking about that all night. He was poor, all right, but I'll be hanged if there wasn't something about him. I took a real liking to him, though I don't really know why!"

Mr. Carson's answer evidently satisfied the Reverend Geiger that the question was only American curiosity and not a challenge to a duel.

"Who was this young man, of whom you speak so warmly?" the pastor asked, taking firm control of the conversation again. I became extremely nervous at this obvious question. The pastor, who was also a high church official, wanted to know to whom in East Berlin I had taken the group. My credentials as a guide were on trial.

Carson answered: "His name was Johann—Hans Johann. He was one of those sort of factory-worker ministers."

The name Johann didn't ring a bell, but the description "factory-worker minister" did. Reverend Geiger quickly realized that I had introduced the group to some of the reform feeling within the church; sensing this, the pastor now warmed up to his task with marked enthusiasm. At the same time he glanced at me with one of those polite unspoken declarations that he now had my number.

"I called my colleagues in the East poor for a good reason, my friend," he began, looking at Mr. Carson.

"They are poor. They are poor in many ways, and no matter which way we look at the picture, if we look at it with open eyes we will see their *real* situation."

"The people of the Zone are obviously poor." (He used the politically loaded term "Zone," meaning Russian Occupation Zone, to show that he did not recognize the German Democratic Republic.) "Look at their shops. Look at their houses. Look in their cupboards. Look at their churches. But this side of their poverty would be easy to carry if it weren't for the fact that they are deprived in other more important areas. Look at what they have to read. Look at what they learn in school. Look at where they are allowed to travel —nowhere! Look at what they are allowed to do. Look at what they are forced to listen to.

"It would be one thing if they were only poor in the pure sense of that term, but besides being poor in the pure sense they are attacked in their misery by an aggressive political monster that calls itself salvation and names their poverty the beginning of Utopia. The party not only robs the poor but pours salt on the sores.

"Any person who is blind to this real situation is unrealistic. Certainly you will always find some opportunists who will sell their birthright for a bowl of porridge, but I plead with you to use your own eyes and make your own judgments. The case is simple enough."

The pastor concluded and sat down to finish his coffee. I noticed that Mr. Carson was studying his every move. He was glaring at him. As we got up to leave Mr. Carson began to talk loudly to the group around him.

"You know," he began, "I think I'm beginning to see something. Something very important, yet something very simple.

"Did you catch the reference of that Reverend Geiger to those people who are willing to sell their birthright for a bowl of porridge? Well, unless I miss my guess he was referring to our friend Johann. He was saying that Johann and those like him have sold out to the Commies for an easy life. He was making a political issue out of a religious one, because of the simple fact that those men like Hans Johann have put the finger on the sore point in this whole business. They see the church for what it is. They see where the church has failed.

"The problem of the church in East Germany is not a political problem but it's a church problem—a religious problem—just as in any other place in the world.

"It's the problem of the old-timer with his set ways and the newcomer with his new ways. It's the problem of the guy who farms with horses and the guy who comes along with a tractor. It's the problem of the guy with the vested interests—yeah, the guy with the vested interests, the good income, the fine buildings, the good show—yeah, it's the problem of priests in their cathedrals and the Methodist circuit rider who comes along with nothing but his pack, his horse, and his Bible.

"It's a religious problem, but they want to make it a political problem. That's the game. All you have to do in the cold war is convince people that the problem is simply a political problem and then you have won the game. If you can call a guy a Commie then you can shut him up! If you criticize the church, then you are a Communist.

"Simple, isn't it?" he asked in triumphant conclusion just as he arrived at the bus.

* * * * *

The deaconess handed out a pile of little blue books about the church and the Wall. Everyone said goodbye all around before getting on board. Mr. Carson was one of the last. He even waited until the Reverend Mr. Gover had thanked the deaconess. Then he approached her and handed her a ball point pen.

"Just a little souvenir," he said.

"How lovely!" she said, surprised. "I shall think of your group every time I write with it."

"And I shall think of you and Reverend Geiger and Pastor Johann every time I write with one like that at home," replied Mr. Carson.

"So distinguished, black and white," the deaconess admired.

Mr. Carson's eye twinkled. "Or white and black. It all depends on how you look at it."

"What?" said the confused deaconess, but it was too late.

The door closed and the bus eased out into the traffic while the big woman waved and then stood alone beside the busy street deciphering the inscription on her gift. It read: Compliments of Carson Implement, Fertile Valley, Minnesota, Your John Deere Dealer.

# PART THREE

## MARXISM

# THE CHRISTIAN-MARXIST DIALOGUE

"Just as the Communists have already helped the church to better understand itself—I mean to free itself from superstition, self-righteous piety, and ideology, so also should the Christians help the Communists to better understand themselves and fulfill their mission of freeing humanity from every oppression, mythology, and inward and outward form of slavery."

This quotation is amazing for many reasons. First of all, it was written by a Marxist, Milan Machovec, professor of philosophy at the Charles University in Prague. Secondly, it was published in Czechoslovakia. Thirdly, it is in a book which deals with theology. Fourthly, it reflects a dialogue now going on in the East between Christians and Marxists which has already graduated from the realm of personal contacts and learned journals.

The development of the present Christian-Marxist dialogue can be traced to many factors. The first and most obvious is the simple fact that following World War II many of the nations of Eastern Europe found themselves with Communist regimes. These were regimes that called themselves Marxist-Leninist. Pictures of Marx appeared everywhere, and quotations from his writings were included in every official speech. Every action that was taken and every decision that was made was justified by his authority.

In the Communist lands of Eastern Europe, however, divergent opinions and understandings of Marx began to develop. It was one thing when Western Marxists, such as leading French and Italian Communists, challenged the official Soviet Stalinist interpretation, but it was quite another thing when "Communists in the colonies" (so to speak) began to question Stalin's interpretation. When this questioning turned into political action, as it did with Tito in Yugoslavia in 1947, Stalin learned his lesson. Tito made his escape, but the rest of Eastern Europe paid for it by being sentenced to a period of savage Stalinist rule and orthodoxy.

The influence of the Stalinist era not only on the developing Christian-Marxist dialogue but also on the whole life of Eastern Europe cannot be underestimated. This reign of terror, which began in the late 1940's and didn't begin to break up until Stalin himself died in 1953, had three profound effects which are important for our discussion. First of all, Stalinism established a dogmatic, simplistic, mechanistic, deterministic interpretation of Marxism, along with a horror-filled political reality which contradicted with its deeds all of the creeds it proclaimed. Secondly, this Stalinist establishment bred its own violent reaction. Disillusionment reached even into the ranks of the oldest hard-core Communists. Resentment and frustration built up until it blew off in the revolutions of East Germany in 1953 and in Poland and Hungary in 1956. But this anti-Stalinist reaction also caused a third effect. Simply said, the third effect of Stalinism was the reopening of all the questions that were left unanswered when Stalinism turned out not to be the answer to social unrest.

But just as Stalinism cannot be overestimated, the effect of its fall must not be undervalued. Anyone who thinks that Communism can't change remains tragically blind to the profound revolution that swept all Eastern Europe in the mid-fifties when the great statues of the Soviet dictator fell and his name was silently removed from cities, streets, and the printed page.

Into the vacuum left by the fall of Stalin exploded all of the intellectual ferment that had been brewing under the pressure of his oppression. This flood of liberated intellectual activity soon found its way to the largest need of the hour: the need to reinterpret Marx. Thus it was that only in the late fifties and the early sixties did the real study of Marx—not the old Socio-Democrat interpretation, or the Stalinist interpretation, or the old revisionist interpretation but a genuine study—really become fashionable.

"There can be no doubt about it," writes the Polish Marxist Adam Schaff in a book published in Warsaw in 1965, "that we are living in an epoch, in which not only broad intellectual circles but also the consuming public is discovering anew the ideology of Marx."

One of the most interesting factors in this current worldwide rediscovery of Marx is the relatively recent "discovery" of some exciting early writings of Marx. Although these papers were discovered, edited, and published in 1932—over 80 years after they were written —it wasn't until the end of the Second World War, and in Eastern Europe not until the fall of Stalin, that these manuscripts were widely read and studied. "This 'discovery,'" writes Adam Schaff, "essentially means that alongside of the traditionally accepted concept of Marx as an economist, Marx as a man of politics, and Marx as a sociologist, the idea of Marx as a humanist is winning importance—if not beginning to overshadow the other interpretations."

As Marxism today tends to become more humanistic, it is obvious that the Marxists must discover that other people who are not Marxists also share these same humanistic concerns. So it is not surprising to find Adam Schaff writing: "Among the creative spirits and defenders of the humanistic cause in the past we find some of history's most noble figures: philosophers, men of politics, and leaders of religious movements. (In the past humanism most often appeared in some sort of religious form, especially in Protestantism and the sects.) All these figures belong to *our* history, to *our* tradition—even the prophets and founders of religious movements, some of whom were canonized and even today are still venerated."

As Marxists thus begin to discover religious thinking, they are first of all shocked to discover how the crude old dogmatic Communist-Marxist criticism and dismissal of Christianity completely missed the mark. Milan Machovec writes: "One is continually astonished by the many persons who claim to be 'Marxists' and yet in their criticism of religion . . . use . . . methods which may be 'radical' but in reality are naive and worthless. Such 'radical critics' who so criticise normally don't have the slightest idea that the Protestant theologians today are themselves also doing this, and usually much more successfully, because they simply know the Bible better!"

This shock of discovering how ill informed some of their fellow Marxists are often leads to another discovery. As Machovec writes: "One may truly say that in a specific way religious thinking today is closer to us than the atheism of yesterday. Simply because it is thinking taking place *today,* it is alive, because it is stimulated by the same questions, difficulties, and problems that we also must solve."

As Marxists in growing numbers thus begin to discover religious thinking, it is also obvious that they discover that many religious thinkers have long been studying Marx, precisely because Marx and the whole complex of questions raised by Communism are one of the biggest questions and one of the biggest problems of today. Marxists are also excited to discover that not all religious thinking about Marx is negative. The foundation for a dialogue is already laid when a Marxist discovers a Protestant philosopher like Erich Thier telling others that: "The young Marx is the discovery of our time!" When Marxists then further discover that some outsiders seem to understand Marx better than some insiders, one can easily say that the framework for an exciting dialogue has been raised. Completely new lines of discussion have been opened when the Polish Marxist Adam Schaff turns against the Soviet Marxist Paschitnow in order to support the Protestant philosopher Erich Thier. "It should be enough," writes Schaff, "when I establish there that—in spite of the fact that I consider myself totally and completely committed to the Communist cause, and in spite of the fact that I am certainly closer to Paschitnow on political questions—in my opinion in his thesis about the anthropology of the young Marx, Thier is right and Paschitnow is wrong!"

So it is that just as one could say that the major problem of the church in East Germany is not the political problem but rather the struggle between the younger reformers and older members of the establishment, so also can one conclude that in political circles in Eastern Europe the major problem is the struggle between the younger "humanistic" Marxist reformers and the older bureaucratic, dogmatic, more Stalinist oriented Communists of the respective establishments. It is only logical that with time the reformers in the church and the reformers in political circles will find each other.

This is in fact happening today. It is happening at a high level, as the books and authors mentioned above demonstrate, but it is also happening in a much less formal way at the grass roots. The real grass roots dialogue is likely to be a rambling conversation between friendly individuals who discover in the course of an evening that they represent opposing points of view and yet they share some common ground.

Such a conversation took place on that cold November evening at the apartment of Hans Johann, the factory worker minister in East Berlin. When our conversation turned to Karl Marx, Hans Johann suddenly stood up and grabbed a folder of papers from his desk. He turned to me and told me that he had written a story about Marx through which he hoped to trick people into having to reevaluate their thinking about this man. It was a story about Marx and yet not about him. Would I like to hear it? Of course.

# THE CONVERSION OF KARL HEINRICH

a Story by Hans Johann

*Another Little In-Between Observation*

This is the story about what happened to a young college student when he graduated from the university and went out into the world to get his first job—which he didn't want. Well, he did and he didn't. He didn't really want the job because he was a philosopher. His dream was to become a teacher—a special kind of teacher. Not a professor at the university. Not the kind of man who is all caught up formally in the academic life, but rather one of those private tutors or instructors who gather around European universities and live in the glow of the intellectual environment without having any of the formal responsibilities. Sort of a free-lance teacher living from the occasional fees students would pay him.

The life as a private tutor might have been possible if it hadn't been for two factors. In 1838 our student's father died. This father and son had been very close. The father was a lawyer in the city of Trier in Germany in the Rhineland on the upper Mosel river valley near the French border. He was Jewish by birth. In fact, he had married the daughter of a well-known Rabbi's family in Amsterdam. The mother and her son were never really close.

When Napoleon fell in 1815 and the Prussian Germans took over in the Rhineland, anti-Jewish laws were established, and the father decided to join the liberal Protestants instead of returning to the ghetto. By 1824 the whole family was baptized.

In 1835 our student, who was the second child and eldest son in this family of eight, went away to the University at Bonn. He was only 17 then. But he was in love. He had fallen in love with his older sister's girlfriend who lived down the street. She was the daughter of a prominent government official and four years older than her lover. Still, in the winter of 1836, when the first semester at the University of Bonn came to an end, the couple became engaged during the semester break.

Then in 1838 the father died. There was no more money. Alone at the University of Berlin and then in Jena our student managed. On the sixth of April, 1841, just after his 23rd birthday, he handed in his doctoral dissertation to the faculty of the University of Jena. So as our story opens in the year of 1842 we find our hero already graduated from the university as a Doctor of Philosophy. He wanted to become a private teacher, but he also wanted to get married! But you can't live on philosophy alone, especially not with a wife. Even for philosophers there is only one alternative—go to work.

At this point along came that Moses Hess saying: "My boy, I've got a job for you!" Nothing could have sounded better to our student. Hess was a radical. He lived and worked as a publisher in Cologne in the Rhineland.

Now the mention of the Rhineland in this connection probably doesn't mean as much to you as it should. When Napoleon first came to power in 1795 the little states of the Rhineland were ceded to France at a meeting in Basel. Suddenly our friend Hess found he was a Frenchman! But more than that he was also a freeman!

You see, Hess was Jewish, and that meant that up until the French came he was kept in the ghetto, but now with everybody yelling "Liberty, Equality, and Fraternity!" Moses Hess finally walked out into a new world. He became a passionate believer in the liberty of personal freedom, equality before the law, and the fraternity of all men no matter what their race, creed, or tongue.

All this lasted 20 years, and then Napoleon had to go and get defeated. When the pompous, pious Prussians annexed the Rhineland citizen Hess became Jewish again. Anti-Jewish laws, established religion, hereditary monarchy, limited suffrage, censorship, and all the rest that went with Friedrich Wilhelm III of Prussia moved back into the Rhineland. Is it any wonder that Moses Hess and others yearned for the good old days of the French?

In any case, as a Cologne publisher Moses Hess had convinced a small circle of enlightened friends to support him in the founding of a little newspaper with which the liberal elements in the area could take pot shots at Prussia. The paper was called "Die Rheinische Zeitung," and now Moses Hess called our student to work on his paper.

Hess was a radical. Our student—Karl Heinrich by name—was also a radical. There was, however, a substantial difference. Hess was a practical radical, while the young man who came to his newspaper was a radical philosopher.

Karl Heinrich started his writing for the newspaper by attacking Prussian censorship. He argued with logic and reasoned that if the Prussian State was the embodiment of right, reason, and morality, as the great philosopher Hegel taught, then Prussia should do away with censorship because this was wrong—it limited freedom. Our young student wielded the weapon of criticism in order to help the state iron out the last inconsistencies between what it was supposed to be and what it was. This was the method of the left-wing followers of Hegel, who worked so hard at their constructive criticism that the state finally condemned them.

Then the day came. As a newspaperman Karl Heinrich was finally forced to attend the assemblies of the local land parliament. He hated it. He drove himself with an inhuman vigor. He was arrogant, confident, and intolerant of all imperfection. He was small in stature with hairy hands and a massive mane of black hair on his head. He was often dressed crudely. His voice was like steel and commanded authority. To say the least, he wasn't very likable. He was restless and impatient with the bungling inefficiency of the local parliament.

Hegel had argued that the great ideas of human history, such as reason, morality, and humanity, were embodied in the Prussian state, and that therefore it was only a matter of time until these ideas drifted down from above to harmonize all human groups such as families, professions, classes, trades, and the like. As Karl Heinrich fussed and fidgeted in his press seat at the local land parliament he questioned anew how much this heap of jabbering idiots could be the embodiment of reason, and if not how long it would be until reason drifted down to enlighten them. In his doctoral dissertation he had already challenged the reality of Hegel's system, but up until now he didn't see clearly what was true reality if Hegel's great ideas of right, reason, and morality were not the central realities of human existence.

Then it happened. The local squirearchy turned to discuss the problem of how to punish the poor who stole decaying wood from the local forests in order to warm their homes and cook their meals. Our young newspaperman sat up in his seat. Before him the landed wealthy who were supposed to represent morality and right told of the poor who crept into the forests at night to steal wood so that their children might stay warm. And these "gentlemen" went on to discuss what punishment might be suitable for such a crime. His eyes burned red as they ignored the plight to discuss the punishment. His face flushed with anger and his body trembled with contempt as they discussed the immorality of the poor. With blazing fury and inexhaustible energy Karl Heinrich stormed from the Parliament hall to his desk to pour out his wrath and indignation, his contempt and condemnation. A prophet was crying. An Amos stood among the cows of Bashan and the priests of Bethel. All of Germany demanded copies of the new *Rheinische Zeitung.*

The censors moved in fast on the *Rheinische Zeitung,* and in March of 1843, only six months after our student had become editor, he was out of a job.

Out of a job, but this time not as a philosophical youth but as a man with a cause. From that day on Karl Heinrich carried with him the hunger and the thirst, the coldness and the misery, of the farmers and workers of the world that he knew. For him they were reality. This was the reality he had been looking for: reality was not Prussian reason drifting down but the masses rising up. It was with them that the force of history, the force of moral right, and the idea of humanity were working toward fulfillment. It was in their hands that the destiny of the world rested. Of this he became convinced.

He was convinced that a society of exploitation was inhuman because it made human things instead of people and that therefore it had to go in order for a human society to come.

He was convinced that this society would not give up on its own but that the poor with moral right on their side would be forced to cast it down in a revolution.

He saw with absolute certainty that it was economics that determined philosophy, morality, religion, and reason, and not vice versa.

And he was convinced that his job was not to interpret the world but to change it.

Well, that's my story. The strange story of the conversion of Karl Heinrich *Marx!*

# My Marx, Your Marx, Karl Marx, and the Marxists' Marx

Hans Johann first told me his story about the conversion of Karl Heinrich Marx one cold November evening at his apartment in East Berlin. He concluded it by saying:

"It all depends on how you look at it. If you have a ball that is half white and half black, you can hold it so that it looks entirely black or you can turn it over so that it looks all white. Karl Marx is like that. According to most official Eastern European lines he is all white, and according to the official line in the West he is all black. His life and contribution are controversial. From the standpoint of the struggling poor workers of Europe in the last century he looks like a prophet, if not a messianic leader. On the other hand, if we look at him from the standpoint of the religious, commercial, and national leaders of that time he looks like a demon emerging from the depths to plague the earth.

"In a sense both the workers and the *status quo* were blind. The workers were blind to the faults of Marx and the *status quo* was blind to the truth in much of his analysis.

"Now if we could isolate Marx from the background of his times or from the prejudices of our own times we might be able to get at some 'true' or 'objective' view of the man Karl Marx. But that is impossible. No one who is anyone comes to Marx cold today.

Everybody has his own opinion, whether based on much research or just a little reading. My little story is my way of looking at him."

During the story Oscar had arrived and taken a seat. He had listened intently to Hans Johann's little story, smiling all the time. Now he took his pipe out as Hans lit his up and answered.

"A very beautiful story," Oscar began.

"A delightful fairy tale but nothing more. Just like Hegel's whole abracadabra about Prussia. What we have to live with here in the German Democratic Republic is not Karl Marx the prophet standing in Cologne like a prophet of old but the Marxists sitting down in the local courthouse passing laws."

For a moment Oscar's eyes flashed and then he got up out of his chair and grabbed the first volume of the bluebound works of Marx and Engels off the book shelf. Flipping the cover open to the introduction, he began to read:

> For the first time in the history of thought Marx and Engels applied dialectical materialism to the phenomenon of society and arrived at the absolutely basic realization that the *intellectual* life of society was determined by the *material* life—that is by the mode of production of material goods—and that the *political* development was determined by the *economics*. They recognized that not from the thoughts of thinkers with their arbitrary discoveries and systems, but rather according to the laws of economic development, a new and higher social order would come into being. This recognition made possible the scientific study of human history in all its details and with all its varieties and contradictions as one process following known laws.
>
> Marx and Engels proved that economic development brought about the fall of the original classless primitive societies and led to the division of society into exploiting and exploited classes. In this society of *antagonistic* classes the struggle between the classes creates the substance of social development, the motor of social progress, the fuel for the climb to a new social order.

Oscar looked up to see if we were listening and then went on to read the concluding sentence with particular emphasis:

> The economic, political, and ideological class struggle of the proletariat *must* sooner or later unavoidably lead to the battle for political power, to the establishment of the dictatorship of the proletariat, to the destruction of Capitalism, and to the creation of a socialist society.

Oscar flipped the book shut with a dramatic gesture and pointed it at Hans, shaking it slightly as he said,

"There, my dear friend, that is the Karl Marx of the Marxists. That is the vulgar Marxism that we have to live with. The Marx of the Marxists is not even a man, he is a crude determinism. A determinism that says that since capitalism is wrong and the workers and farmers are right, the workers and farmers are predestined to destroy the wrong and establish the right. The battle for political power—the revolution—must come. Capitalism must be destroyed, and the new society must be good because it is built by the good guys."

Oscar stood up to return the book to its shelf. On the way he smiled and commented,

"I'm afraid that your student-turned-newspaper-editor-turned-prophet-of-the-poor has created a monster. He has told the workers that they are destined to rule, and they have fanatically believed his revelation. He fired them up with volumes of pseudoscientific abracadabra and sent them off to a revolution. Now those who wear the name of Marx sit in the seats of power and, I ask you, what has changed? Nothing! There are still the exploiters and the exploited.

"You see nothing really has changed. Today Walter Ulbricht is the Kaiser. Marxism is the Hegelianism that teaches that our state is the culmination of human history. Marxism is the philosophy that teaches that because we are a farmers' and workers' state we are the embodiment of reason and morality. Marxism is the religion which teaches that all things which appear bad are really only illusions, because the state is good."

Suddenly Oscar's eyes flashed, and he sat a little forward in his chair, indicating that he had found something that he felt it was important to have said.

"Now this observation that there is really no basic difference between the Prussia of old and the German Democratic Republic of today brings us to a second delightfully entertaining observation. Today the farmers and the workers of the first German farmers' and workers' state—the German Democratic Republic—are all Marxist in at least one point.

"You and I know that 80 to 90 per cent of the farmers and workers of our state are opposed to the state. They keep peeking over the border at West Germany and asking why they have to suffer with long hours, cramped quarters, empty shops, continual political propaganda, and the lot when they are supposed to be the liberated workers and their West German comrades are supposed to be the exploited ones. Their conclusion is easy: that they are not the liberated but the exploited ones.

"Now it is exactly at this point that the Marxism that has rubbed off on them begins to show up. Vulgar Marxism teaches that a class conflict must necessarily culminate in a revolution—it must come, so it is determined. And vulgar Marxism also teaches that the farmers and workers should work with history to bring about the revolution, to bring about that glorious day when the exploiters shall fall and exploitation shall be no more.

"So to the vexation of our ruling German Democratic Marxists, the whole proletariat is unconsciously following the vulgar Marxist creed to the letter and working for the downfall of the government of the exploiters and the establishment of a reign of material benefit like that promised by vulgar Marxism and found in West Germany."

Oscar laughed at the irony of the situation that he had just pictured and then went on:

"That's why there is so much passive resistance and dragging of the feet in our factories and on our farms. The workers and farmers believe that by so doing they will hurt the economy and hasten the day when everything will collapse and the glorious day of the revolution and liberation will come. What could be more Marxist?

"And according to your Marx—my dear friend—you should be helping them. Didn't you say that Marx—your Marx—felt that there was no hope of reforming the state, so that the only viable alternative was revolutionary activity? Okay, then, my friend. Into the Underground for Marx's sake."

Oscar sat back in his chair again, smiling triumphantly at this little provocative jab with which he had ended his dissertation. Actually both Oscar and Hans were on the same side. They were both members of that small group within East Germany who were trying to make the best of things. They were both extremely critical of the government. In fact, they were both critical of all injustice no matter where it might be, and they saw their calling as Christians as somehow related to the mission of reconciling conflicts and eliminating oppression no matter where it might be.

* * * * *

At this point the door opened and Mrs. Johann ushered in a man moderate in stature, friendly in appearance, accented by heavy glasses, and dressed in a sport coat with an open shirt underneath. On his lapel he wore a "bonbon" as the Germans call it. Actually it is the pin that marks the wearer as a member of the ruling East German Socialist Unity Party. Hans introduced the man to us as Emil Kotowski.

Actually Hans and Oscar and I were supposed only to be observers this evening. In the beginning this evening had been arranged so that a rather prominent American professor visiting and lecturing in West Berlin might be able to have a conversation with Mr. Kotowski. When this American professor made his plans to come to Berlin some months ago he had written to ask whether it wouldn't be possible to arrange some sort of informal contact with people on the other side. The request was passed on to Hans and some other friends in the East who in turn approached some of the men in the East German government who occasionally let their hair down a bit in informal situations. Mr. Kotowski had said that he would be honored to spend an evening with the American professor, or for that matter with anyone who wanted to come. In fact, Mr. Kotowski was one of those friendly men usually found in any group who are always willing to visit and discuss even though it is known from the very beginning that there will be a difference of viewpoints at the meeting.

The American professor was excited about the meeting, but when his host in West Berlin had found out he had exploded. "That is impossible! You can't go to East Berlin, not to visit with a Communist Party official! Why, it would be all over the newspapers the next day! It is only a trick to use you!"

I was shaken by this reaction.

It was this kind of wall of fear and fantasy that had cut off communications long before the wall of brick and mortar was built. And this wall of prejudice was built by both sides.

We explained to Mr. Kotowski what had happened as Mrs. Johann brought in some wine and Hans filled the glasses all around. Mr. Kotowski said that perhaps it was better to be among ourselves on this wintry evening.

"I don't know your professor," he said, "but I do feel that I know the rest of you here, and that means that we won't have to go through all the preliminaries before we settle down to a real discussion."

Hans proposed a toast to "Friendship" and we all drank. The evening was under way, but little did I suspect at that point what the outcome would be. Oscar sat in an overstuffed chair. Hans sat in the desk chair turned out from the desk to face the room. I sat in a straight-backed table chair, and Mr. Kotowski shared the couch with Mrs. Johann, who sat most of the evening knitting quietly.

"Well, what have you all been discussing?" Mr. Kotowski asked, turning to Hans. "Your wife tells me that you have already been hard at it."

Oscar answered the question. "Marxism. As you came in I was just trying to convince Hans that according to his romantic view of Marx he still didn't have any alternative but to join the revolutionary forces working to throw off the yoke of exploitation."

Oscar left the issue open by not naming just who the exploiters were, therefore allowing for the usual party line explanation that the capitalists were the only exploiters. Hans knew Mr. Kotowski well enough to know that they could speak openly, and so he sketched in the conversation up to this point and then turned on Oscar to get in his licks.

"When I say that I am a Marxist, that doesn't mean that I follow the master hook, line, and sinker. As a man who compassionately gave his life in the battle against man's inhumanity to man, I stand in awe of him and I'm humbled by him. As the man who taught me the value of material factors in influencing social and civil codes, I feel indebted to him.

"However, the Marxists have tried too hard to make a dogmatic Marxist out of Marx. Just as the Lutherans are always trying to baptize Luther into their systematic theology, the Marxists are always trying to fit Marx to their system.

"The Marxists have built a system out of what Marx has said, and now they try to force every situation, every land, every war, every revolution, and every antagonism into their system. They are trying to hammer round pegs into square holes.

"For example, they argue that revolution must come and that revolution is the only way. But what Marx gave his life for was the end of man's inhumanity to man. At one point in his development Marx was convinced that this goal of his could be reached only through a revolution. Yet in his later years he saw the possibility of other methods. In 1872 in a public address in Amsterdam Marx himself said that the workers must one day have the political power in their hands, but that did not mean that the way to that power was the same in every situation. He went on to say that in lands like England and America and perhaps Holland there is every reason to believe that the workers can arrive at their goal with peaceful means. Marx himself allowed for evolution instead of revolution."

"Well, well, this is most interesting," said Mr. Kotowski. "I come to visit a group of Christians, and what do I find them doing? Discussing Marxism. What better way is there for me to enter the conversation than to start talking about Christianity?"

Mr. Kotowski sat comfortably on the couch smoking a cigarette. Hans leaned back in his chair indicating that he yielded the conversation to his guest. Mr. Kotowski spoke:

"I think we can best understand the situation if we compare Marxism with Christianity. As you have already indicated, Marxism is sort of a religion. But just as there is little relation between Christ and the Christians, so too there is little relation between Marx and the Marxists. It is difficult to find the connection between the pomp and pageantry of the church and the piety and poverty of the Christ. Is it any wonder then that it is difficult to find the connection between the poison of the Marxists and the passion of Marx?

"Marxism too has had its reformers. By the turn of the century there were two defined sects. The first contained the orthodox, who were revolutionary and nondeterminist. Then along came Lenin arguing that the proletariat was predestined to rule but because they didn't know it yet the Party was predestined to bring the proletariat to its enlightenment, and the leader—Lenin himself—was predestined to lead the Party to its role of leading the people. To say the least, he considered himself in a messianic role. He was followed by Stalin, a fat priest type who butchered all the prophets that were left and settled down to call his hell the promised heaven.

"Today Marx and Engels as well as Lenin and Stalin are dead, and the faith is up for grabs. What is Marxism? Is it the picture of Marx that you have, Hans? Is it the modification of Engels? Is it the socialism of the early pre-World War I Revisionism? Is it Lenin's democratic centralism? Is it Stalin's totalitarianism? Is it Tito's Yugoslavian way? I don't know!

"Leszek Kolakowski, the Polish philosopher, defines Marxism not as a doctrine, which can only be accepted or rejected, not a universal system—but rather as a living, philosophical inspiration inside of the general world view, an impulse which works on in the social intelligence and memory of mankind, and which thanks for its continual influence the new and still valuable points of view which the spirit of Marx has given us."

* * * * *

A knock at the door interrupted Mr. Kotowski. Now we realized that we were in East Berlin. Mrs. Johann sat up and said, "Who could that be?" Everyone was uneasy. It wasn't that anyone thought of the police, it was just that our group was such a mixture. How would Mr. Kotowski explain spending an evening with an American? How could the two East Germans explain a Party member in their presence? Everyone was nervous. Hans got up and went out into the hall. We all listened as he opened the apartment door.

"Gerhard," Hans greeted, "what brings you out on this night?"

"Oh, that must be the pastor of the local church," Mrs. Johann said, relaxing. "He often drops in like this. He's a bit of the old school."

Mr. Kotowski looked uneasy. Pastor Gerhard Hess entered the room. He was tall and slender and his hair was still wet from the snow. He kept saying that he didn't want to interrupt, but Hans encouraged him to come in and introduced him to the others. He took another one of the dining room chairs and Hans poured him a glass of wine.

The pastor was nervous and looked very uneasy. His clothes hung loosely on his tall body. Hans encouraged him to speak, and finally the dam broke and his story flooded out:

"They came and got my boy last night. At ten o'clock in the evening two policemen appeared and asked if this was the home of Friedrich Gerhard. I said 'Yes,' and they asked to see him. When the boy appeared, they asked him to pack some of his things; he was under arrest. He packed and they took him away. The charge: conspiring to flee from the German Democratic Republic. All day long I have been at the office of my lawyer and at the police station. We don't know where he is, and my lawyer won't be able to get through for at least a week yet."

"Did you know he was planning on fleeing to the West?" Hans asked, sitting forward and listening intently.

"Of course," the pastor answered, continuing:

"I mean, we didn't know he was down to the specifics. After all, he was 18. We knew he couldn't stand it here. He wanted a life like other young people. We would have been in the West long ago if we hadn't been convinced that God needed us here. And he does. God has given us amazing strength. The congregation has dwindled away. All of those that do show up for confirmation today have already been to the Youth Consecration Ceremony. We've been attacked on every side by the onslaughts of Communist atheism. Yet we've held services every Sunday. Our front was held. We've been used to help other lives, even lives of Communists.

"But today I almost broke. They're destroying the church. Every day we hear that Marx taught that religion is just a myth created to justify the capitalist and pacify the proletariat. They are convinced that the church will die away, so they are just ignoring it, waiting for it to fall. Every now and then they come over and give it a shake to see how the process of dying out is coming—and one of these days it will fall. Oh, I fear it. God knows we've tried. God knows . . . ."

The pastor stopped in the middle of his sentence. His hands gripped the chair and his eyes opened wide. He had just seen the "bonbon," the Communist Party pin on Mr. Kotowski's suit jacket. He looked at Hans for some sign. He began to turn white.

"Yes," said Mr. Kotowski, "I am a member of the Party; but I am also a human being and I also have a son.

"Mr. Hess," Mr. Kotowski continued, "your son will be all right. I can assure you of that. Remember, Stalin is dead. There is now due process of law in the German Democratic Republic. Three million people fled the GDR before the Wall. Three million of our 17 million. We cannot allow that. There have to be laws against it. Your son will be given a fair trial, and because he is guilty, as you yourself admit, he will be sentenced to perhaps two years. If all goes well, he should be out in less than a year. There have been hundreds of such cases already, and there will undoubtedly be hundreds of such cases in the future. Almost all of those sentenced are released early.

"If I may be so bold in the confines of this group of friends," Mr. Kotowski continued, looking seriously at the pastor, "might I suggest that your real problem with your son is his desire to flee—and not the problem that he has been caught in the act of preparing to flee?

"If you only live to hold up a decaying church against the force of history, and if your son lives only for the cars, clothes, and cuisine of the West, then both you and your son will never be happy here. Instead you will both be lusting continually after another world. You will be like so many other citizens of our land: Dissatisfied. Restless. Plotting. Frankly, Pastor, I am disturbed by your attitude—I expected more from a man of the cloth."

"It is more than cars, clothes, and cuisine that we live for," the pastor answered, composing himself. "We live for the freedom to say what we think, to go where we want, to worship as we feel called to."

"Wait a minute," Mr. Kotowski said, undertaking to answer. "Who has the right to give you the freedom to speak or to take it away—the state? Or do you bind your own selves in slavery with your own fear of speaking? Don't you always preach that freedom is from God? And if you are talking about society's limits on speech, what makes you think that you won't feel curtailed in West Germany?

"And when you talk of the freedom to go where you want, remember it was your own God who kept you here and your own God who helped you see that it was wrong to go West for meat and drink only because the West was watered with dollars and therefore recovering faster than the East where everything lies in the ruins of war.

"And when you talk of worship, you yourself have said that you have had services every Sunday. Let me ask you a question: Is your God limited? Has your God fled the German Democratic Republic?"

"You're being unfair," said Hans, breaking in.

"Oh, I know it," said Mr. Katowski, apologizing immediately. "But don't you see?" he continued, leaning forward and looking intently at the pastor. "Don't you see that with your whole attitude you have built up a wall against our society? You have made your situation an either/or choice. You have made it black and white, where it is all gray. You have built up a Christian front against Eastern atheism. Instead of building bridges you have built a wall, a front.

"Of course, in many ways I don't blame you. I am speaking openly now and in confidence among friends. In many ways I don't blame you for building a wall. Our Party has so many little idiots in it, little men who have now become rulers and like the village schoolteachers are ready to show off their power. Don't you think I go crazy working with them? Trying—oh, God knows how we try—to get them to stop trying to pound round pegs into square holes. Sure, if you had met me in public you would have thought probably that I was just another one of those incorrigibles. But I have no respect for the human being who doesn't go beyond the facade to discover the man behind the mask he is forced to wear.

"What do you think we see when we look at the church? Pompous, pious little priests prancing around pooh-poohing everything we say just because we say it. Don't you understand that there are little men everywhere? My father was an old Social Democrat of the left wing, and because some little Hitler-loving pastor called him a Communist he spent four years in a concentration camp. I probably would hate the church today if my father hadn't met some really great Christians in the concentration camp, men he couldn't ignore. Men who came to our home after the war and sat at our table. Men who learned from us and men who, I am not ashamed to admit, taught us much.

"It was from Christianity that Karl Marx and Marxism learned its zeal for human justice and its dream of a better society—I don't care what the others say. And it was from Marx that the church learned that it wasn't creeds that were preached but deeds that were done which mattered.

"Anyone is a fool who thinks today that serious Marxists dismiss Christianity with a wave of the hand. Just as Marx helped challenge Barth, Hromadka, and in America Niebuhr to a new vision of the faith, so Barth, Hromadka, and Niebuhr have forced the Marxists to reevaluate Christianity. And just as we are discovering you, some of your men are discovering us. Look at Hans and Oscar here. And even this American Christian Marxist!

"You see, you Christians with your emphasis on original sin balanced out by the *Imago Dei* humanism help us to counteract our optimism about the proletariat with realism about humanity. And we Marxists can help you see the need of transforming creeds into deeds."

Mr. Kotowski hadn't finished yet, even though his words stopped. He waited for a minute, still looking tense, and then he concluded:

"A Christian should never live just to be against something. That is a negative life, just as negative as a life dedicated only to anticapitalism. The Christian, if he is a Christian, must live for others—and if that be the case, then God knows we need you here."

Mr. Kotowski stopped. The pastor was sitting very still in his chair. Everyone was quiet. The pastor looked at Mr. Kotowski for a long time, and then his lips began to form a question that came out very slowly.

"I know my son will be all right. But do you think—well, I mean—would you have any way—could you—perhaps find out where he is and if he is—if he needs anything?"

Mr. Kotowski answered, "I'll do what I can. There are always

ways and channels which are open, and it is seldom that there is no way. I'll see what I can find out, and I'll call you tomorrow."

Oscar let out a big sort of laugh that rather surprised everyone. Then still smiling he said, "Well, that sort of completes the circle. A Marxist comes over to the home of some Christian friends and finds them discussing Marx, and a Pastor comes to the same house with a problem to lay before his brothers and a Marxist ends up helping him. Oh, wonderful, strange world in which we live!"

Then Oscar looked right at me and asked, "Tell me, great Father, does anything like this ever happen in the West? Don't you want to come over here and join us?"

Everybody joined in this bit of fun, and Hans poured more wine as the guests relaxed to less strained conversation.

# PART FOUR

# SOLUTIONS

# CHRIST AND THE ROSA LUXEMBURG COLLECTIVE FARM

Collectivization of agriculture in East Germany came in the spring of 1960. Up until then the Communists left the farms in the German Democratic Republic alone. After all, Poland had been collectivized in the Stalinist era only to be decollectivized again by Gomulka following the Polish revolution of 1956.

But for a reason which still puzzles many liberal Party men, in the spring of 1960 the pressure was on in the GDR to collectivize. For a while there was a return to Stalinist methods as troops of convincers came out to the farms to follow the farmers day and night into every room of the house until the farmer was convinced that collectivization was the best. There had been a lot of stories in those days about loudspeakers blaring and spotlights shining night after night. On the 12th of April, 1960, the last farmer was convinced, and East Germany was collectivized. Cattle were herded together and fields plowed together. Machinery was driven to common machinery parks.

It had all sounded good on paper, but it resulted in a horrible mess. Fields didn't get planted, cattle died, tractors and other machines rusted out. For the years of 1961 and 1962 meat disappeared for days on end from the markets. Potatoes were rationed again. Only now, slowly but surely, the recovery was being made.

I had just met Ilse in East Berlin at a church rally during the height of the East German collectivization drive in the spring of 1960. A group of Westerners at this meeting were asking why the East German Christians didn't resist more. Ilse stood up. She was a young woman of perhaps thirty then. Her eyes were dark, her hair ebony black, her manner earnest.

"You see," she pleaded, "that is what we all must learn, that we are to love, not to resist. And we here do really love our land—how could it be otherwise? This responsibility to our land is our mission and no one else can render it for us. It is our responsibility to be the conscience of our state! To be the conscience not out of hate, but precisely because we love her so much that we cannot stand to look on when the state itself, its people, or its government, does that which is wrong. One thing must always be clear in our witness: What we do, we do out of love and in love. We always point that out over here. Christians must never battle *against* others, but always struggle *for* others. And even if the world can't quite grasp this fact, at least among us Christians the point should be clear."

These words had been my introduction to Ilse. Now as I concluded another afternoon visit to her collective farm home in East Germany she finally opened up and told me the story behind her outburst of that first meeting.

"In those days of the forced collectivization drive," she began, "I was at the university. I had a good friend in my required Political Philosophy class who was very active in the Free German Youth Movement. When the push came to collectivize the two of us went at it long and hard. My friend—his name was Ludwig—argued that in this day and age collectivization was necessary to be good stewards of the land. At first I opposed this. I was a true liberal in those days. I defended the right of the individual farmers to run their own lives and farms. Ludwig countered by asking if citizens in a society didn't have a responsibility to the society as a whole. Ludwig argued that the farmers as members of the society had a responsibility to feed the rest of society, which in turn produced tools, communications, conveniences, and so forth for the farmer—to say nothing of the larger social benefits such as medicine, education, and protection Ludwig argued that it was unreasonable to allow independent little farmers to threaten and curtail the whole agricultural production just so that they could have their little independent farms. Ludwig summed up his case by contending that the agriculture of the nation was more important than the independence of the farmers:

"I was finally convinced, not by the argument of responsibility, but by the obvious consideration that collectivized agriculture was better stewardship of resources than the unendlessly divided inherited German farm pattern with its unending reduplication of tools, labor, and effort.

"I was moody in those days. I saw that the answer was not as simple as I wanted. My farm friends who were directly involved in the harassments poured out their plight to me. I saw that the farmers would not change on their own, but I also saw that the methods used by the government were wrong. It came to a direct conflict one day when Ludwig and a group of Free German Youth were to go to a district rally in an area near Niederfeld where I had grown up.

"As I said, I was idealistic then, so I went out to the Rally. When the commissar asked for questions I got up and started attacking the whole method of collectivization. I condemned the convincers. I called them Nazi-like thugs and a disgrace to a democratic republic. People clapped and cheered and the commissar called for order. It took them a long time to get things quieted down, and afterwards when one of the Free German Youth radicals started calling me names and threatening to knock my block off, the police, thinking it was a fight, arrested both of us.

"At first I was in jail in Niederfeld and then I was moved to Leipzig. Soon the charges against both of us were dismissed."

As Ilse concluded her story I finally began to see more clearly why she and a group of her friends from the student congregation had volunteered for this collective farm after they had finished the university.

This move of theirs had so fascinated me at that time that I had secured a visa and made my first visit to the farm the following summer. On the way down I had noticed the broad open fields of East Germany, which were now in direct contrast to the small intensely cultivated plots of West Germany. Every now and then I had noticed a cluster of new buildings which marked the location of a new collective farm.

I can still vividly remember how upset I was when I made that first visit to the Rosa Luxemburg Collective Farm. Ilse had changed so. She was quiet and serious. She had chosen for herself the job of tending the cattle barn. This tired her, but most of all the mismanagement and the bad planning of the farm disturbed her. She seemed glad to have someone to talk to. She told me of the old farmer who had committed suicide in the neighborhood. The old man just couldn't stand to give up his cattle, which had become almost members of his family. Fortunately, she told me, on this farm no one had taken his life, although the countryside was full of stories of suicides.

She introduced me to an elderly man who eyed us suspiciously. When we were alone she explained that the old man had once had a big farm of his own, although now he was just a laborer on the collective farm.

While I was visiting Ilse at the farm that time I met some of the young agricultural experts who had been assigned to run the operation. It was easy to see how their arrogance would breed dissension among the members of the farm. They were later removed.

That period had been a time of chaotic disorganization for the farmers and the farm. Ilse confessed that she had chosen to take care of the cattle because she felt sorry for them, because they were often left uncared-for. The collectivized farmers so hated the collectivization that they refused to work longer than the required nine hours a day. Often this meant that they would leave the cattle unattended. Ilse poured out her mixed feelings about this hard encounter with humanity. As for the farmers, many of whom still clung to the church, she said she could understand their resentment, but she couldn't forgive their callousness. As for the Communists, she could understand their reasons for collectivization but not their inhumanity.

At that time I hadn't really understood why she had chosen such a life in spite of all her explanations.

As I drove home from the now famous Rosa Luxemburg Collective Farm her words spoken years ago when I had made that first visit finally made sense.

"The church," she had said, "has two doors open to it over here: the door to the world and the door to the ghetto. If we choose the ghetto, we will be committing suicide, because the church is not a human grouping with a value in and of itself. The church only lives because it has a commission—a job to do.

"This means that when our church here in East Germany is no longer allowed to relax in the parlor of society, then it must avoid the ghetto, no matter how comfortably furnished it is, and search out the servants' quarters. The apostles called themselves 'servants' or 'slaves' of Jesus Christ. To be a servant of Christ means to be ready to jump to the service of the Lord when he calls through the voice of our troubled brothers. He has called us here—to the Rosa Luxemburg Collective Farm—and here we gladly serve."

# HORST AND THE NEUSTADT TEAM EXPERIMENT

I had first met Horst at a conference held in the offices of a mission society located in East Berlin. A number of ministers had gathered there, along with a theologian from Holland, to discuss the nature of the congregation. There I had first heard of Neustadt. Neustadt means "the new city." When the Communists built Neustadt they of course didn't waste any money on building a church. It wasn't that they were opposed to it, it was just that at that time they had more important things to build.

As a young theological student in Leipzig, Horst had accepted this challenge. When he graduated from his work at the university he moved to Neustadt as a worker. He was considered a radical. He agreed with the Communists that the church wasn't necessary —or at least the church building. In fact, he soon saw that a parish in the traditional style would be impossible to build in this new situation. Somehow a big church with a parish hall and classrooms didn't fit. Even the minimum requirements of a room for a pastor's apartment and office couldn't be found in this town where there was a waiting list for every available room. So this young theological student had just worked in the factory and watched and waited for the Holy Spirit.

Friends from the theological school had often visited Horst in Neustadt in those days, and so it came about that two of them decided to join Horst to form a team ministry to Neustadt. There was already a Christian group in the town large enough to support one of the three theologically trained men to devote full time to the pastorate while the others worked. Thus Horst's friends moved to Neustadt.

Today as Horst and his friends took me for a walk around Neustadt people continually greeted us from their balconies. Horst seemed to know everyone; he called child after child by his first name. Occasionally he would comment on some person, saying, "That's Schmidt, he works in the mill," or, "That's Joseph, he comes from Poland and works on my crew."

There was no evidence here that this was Sunday except for the fact that no one was working. Clotheslines were filled and everyone was in sports clothes. Some of the men were washing their cars.

"Do you see that building?" Horst asked. "When I first came here the only known Christians in Neustadt lived in that building. Schneider was their name. Every Sunday they would get on their bicycles and head off over the hill back there for the next town. It's four kilometers. The pastor over there saw his chance and he kept coming over here visiting. He kept wanting to sort of set up office with the Schneiders, but nobody came. When the baby came and Schneiders got tied down to their building they were forced to make contact with some neighbors. Still nobody could get through to them. As time went on they sort of turned their apartment into a religious ghetto where they withdrew from the Communist world. When I arrived here some people had given up on them and most people considered them some sort of religious fanatics.

"The first time I visited with them it was like some cell meeting or something. You'd think Christians were some sort of Martians or something from outer space. All night long they whined and moaned about how hard it was to keep up their Christian beliefs in these hostile surroundings. Nobody kept the Sabbath. Nobody prayed. Nobody believed in God. Nobody went to church. Even the pastor didn't come any more."

Horst was laughing to himself as we went by the building that he was talking about.

"I guess I made a fool of myself that night. I said, 'Why on earth are you sitting here crying about how bad you've got it and about how you don't have any friends? The Good Lord didn't put you here to be ministered to, but to minister.' That sort of shook them up and inside of a week we were the best of friends. Finally we started Bible studies together every now and then."

Horst glanced at me with a puzzled look and went on.

"You know, it's funny how people suddenly discover Christ when they read the Bible. Suddenly he isn't up there on the altar or in the stained glass window, but he's right next to you on the line or next door to you in the block.

"Schneider began to visit people, not to get them to go to church like before but just to visit them because they were neighbors; and you know, now he's one of the best-liked men in town. He's a leader of the Young Pioneers. Don't tell the preacher—he'd flip."

As we rounded the corner the last member of the team came toward us. This man—Fritz—was the only ordained man. Ordination had been a problem with the group. Horst explained:

"What should we do? There we were, all of a sudden a congregation of about twenty people who agreed to bind ourselves together in the name of Christ with a common discipline in order to—to minister to this community, if you please.

"Three of us were theologically trained, but the others didn't have the formal classical training, and yet in the Bible studies and discussions which were becoming the worship services of our community, they led just as much as anybody else. We had a doctor, two engineers, a manager, two school teachers, and the rest workers. They all gave the same of their time and money.

"According to the old pattern, only the minister is ordained and the others are just out-of-date. We haven't got an old-fashioned one-man show, and we couldn't theologically allow for any such special division as an old-fashioned ordination. We had big arguments about it in those days. Not to be ordained brought us in for all sorts of problems with the established church that sponsored us, or at least tolerated us. To be ordained meant to break faith with the principle of group fellowship which is the backbone of our life here. There was no way around it. We are going a new way out here.

"Fritz rescued us," Horst continued. "He was already ordained when he moved in to join us. At least for the time being, for the record, we have one legal 'Herr Pastor.' Yet our real authority is not our paper and pastoral connection through legal Fritz to the established church, but our mission and our commission from our 'Herr Gott.' Among ourselves and those who agree to share the discipline with us, we share the office that was once carried by one man. Actually Fritz, there, works in the factory, while Theo is the one free for pastoral work right now."

"That's what my father can't see," commented one of the other men. "He still doesn't understand why we can't just build another church here and set down another man. With so many villages without a pastor he thinks it's a crime that we have four theologically trained men here now, with three of them in the factories and only one of them ordained."

"Not only your father!" chimed in Horst, smiling back. "Last week old Blimpbottom of the Regional Church stopped by again. (Horst stood back, folded his big hairy hands in imitation of the minister under consideration, and puckering up his mouth he began to impersonate the man with all sorts of little facial gestures.) 'My dear brother. Now that you have done such wonderful organizational work here in Neustadt the regional church is prepared to build a church here and thereby free the other members of your intensive work for needed service in other areas of serious affliction.' "

Horst dropped his imitation and turning to me he pleaded:

"Can't they get it through their little heads that we are living in new times? You can't have priests living on the outside any more. You've got to have prophets living and working in and with the people of God. They want an established church. We want the freedom of disestablishment. They want a respected place in the community. We want the respect by virtue of the service, and if the service—the compassionate ministry of those who have the audacity to call themselves followers of Christ—if their ministry stinks, then we aren't afraid to hear it. They want the work, as they so affectionately call it, supported by dues collected by the machinery of the state along with the taxes, but the state won't do that over here and they shouldn't. The church must learn to trust God enough to live from his gifts. You might have to pray in a Catholic church, but at least your conscience will be clean."

"We don't know where we're going, exactly," Horst continued, "but we know where we can't go. We can't go back to the Middle Ages, and we can't transfer the Middle Ages into the twentieth century. The Altar is no longer married to the Throne. The days of Christian states—if there ever was such a thing—the days of throne and altar are over. Christians today must exist as the leaven in the loaf and not as the whole loaf. Christians today must be the salt which gives the meat its flavor and not the almighty pot roast itself. Not a Christian world over against a pagan world, but one world with Christians in there leading the way. This is all we are trying to do in Neustadt."

# EASTER

I swung the wheel hard to the left and the car sped onto the broad new highway which, according to the sign, led to Neustadt. Up ahead in the valley the new city was visible. It looked like a drawing in a magazine on city planning. Tall blocks of apartments stood in green parks with smaller public buildings located here and there. In the center of the complex were the remnants of the village which had once dominated this landscape. Behind the old village stood the factory complex. Tall chimneys looked from this distance like candles on a birthday cake with little wisps of smoke coming from them. There must have been five or six sections of apartment buildings forming various parts of the city.

Driving into Neustadt was like driving into a new world, for here everything was new. The city itself was entirely post-war and had been built up to accompany the industrial development which had been located here. Both factory and town were new.

Indeed, Neustadt was one of eight or nine socialist cities built up newly in the German Democratic Republic around new industrial developments. As soon as you left the fields and started driving between the apartment houses you noticed two things. First of all, there were children everywhere. This showed that the community was made up mostly of young people. Secondly, there were cars parked everywhere, which showed the relative wealth of these workers.

Jubilation broke out as we pulled up in front of the apartment building.

"You made it! Oh, halleluia, you're here! It is so wonderful that you could come for my wedding," Theo shouted. I can't really remember what happened next, everything happened so fast. I was shaking hands and hearing names. Then I was moving up steps and then there were more people shaking hands, greeting, smiling, questioning, all standing and talking at once.

The room was filled with books on all walls. Somewhere in the background a record was playing. Flowers stood in vases on every table. Modern prints done by an artist in Berlin hung in dramatic spots on the wall. The furniture was modern, with bright colors set off by pillows and covers obviously made by some mother or auntie who wasn't quite up on the modern taste in fabric.

I was given a cup of coffee and a sandwich and told to hurry up, as Theo was ready to leave for the courthouse for the civil ceremony. In Europe the civil marriage always precedes the church ceremony. In East Germany many citizens just let it go with the mayor's knot tied in the courthouse, and vows repeated in the church are the exception, not the rule.

As Theo was driving off to the courthouse, we started out on the walk to the church. The civil ceremony was scheduled for 1:30 and the church service for two.

Horst joined me on the way to the church. He was a stocky, heavily built man in his early thirties. His face was weathered and his hands were mammoth.

"It's really wonderful that you could come," he greeted me as he came up alongside. "It isn't every day that we have a church wedding here, and this is the first time we have had an American guest."

After a while we left the modern park of apartment houses and entered the cluster of old buildings which marked the old village. There in the middle of the small square was a little old stone church. A crowd of people were gathered around outside.

"Why, that's a Catholic church!" I exclaimed, as I saw a statue of Mary on the facade.

"Catholic-Watholic!" answered Horst. "The days when we could allow ourselves the luxury of denominations are gone. The Christians around here are so few you don't go getting uppity about labels. They keep the kneeling pads dusted with their masses and we keep the pews dusted with our sermons. We're just lucky this old chapel is left here; otherwise we'd be in some clubroom or something with Marx and Lenin staring down at us all the time."

Horst excused himself to go up to the choir loft. His wife was the organist and he had promised to turn pages. The bell began to ring and we entered the church. Some of the people genuflected, showing that they were Catholics.

As the bells stopped the organ swelled. The prelude was based on the chorale *Lobet den Herrn*—Praise to the Lord. In front, just before the altar, there were two chairs. The pastor came out of the sacristy and stood facing the altar for a short prayer before he turned to face the congregation. He stood perfectly framed by the gothic arches of the chapel, highlighted by the richly carved altar behind him. The organ ended the prelude and people began pulling out their hymn books and checking the number hung on the hymn board on the wall. With the first chord of the hymn everyone burst into praise: "Praise to the Lord, the Almighty, the King of Creation." Oh, what a hymn! I've been at a lot of weddings, but this one today deep behind the Iron Curtain was by far the most moving.

The pastor left the altar and went down the aisle. He returned leading the bride and the groom to the two chairs in front of the church. They stood there now, facing the altar and framed with the pastor by the arches. At the end of the hymn the congregation rose and the pastor began with: "In the name of the Father and of the Son and of the Holy Spirit, Amen." The congregation stood as we confessed together and prayed together. Then everyone was seated. Even the bride and groom.

"Theo and Sabine," the pastor addressed them, "on this your wedding day I want to give you as your wedding verse the words of our Lord, recorded in the Gospel according to John, the twentieth chapter, the twenty-first verse: 'Peace be with you. As the Father has sent me, even so I send you.' "

The pastor closed the wedding Bible out of which he had read the text and which he would give to the newlyweds at the end of the service. Looking them in the eye, he addressed them.

He spoke first of their obligation to love each other.

Then he spoke of their obligation to love God.

Thirdly, he called upon them to love the unlovable. He spoke softly and earnestly. "This story is set in the Easter season. Good Friday is in the past, and the triumphant Lord stands now before his disciples in the glory of his resurrection and says to them, 'Peace be with you.' The peace of the Lord is given you today in your new life together. But there is little peace in this land and in this world. Therefore as the Lord has come to bless you, so he sends you forth to bless the outcast and downtrodden. Let your door never be closed. Let your table never be too crowded when the stranger comes. Let your schedule never be too full when neighbors need friends. Let your world never be closed to the least of these your brothers, the hungry, the thirsty, the strangers, the naked, the sick, and the imprisoned."

The Pastor ended his charge and raised his voice to intone: "In the name of the Father and of the Son and of the Holy Spirit, Amen."

The congregation rose and the couple fell to their knees as the pastor prayed with his arms symbolically crossed and his hands on their heads. Then he blessed them, making the sign of the cross with big bold strokes, and the organ swelled with the hymn, *Grosser Gott, wir Loben dich,* Great God, We Praise Thee, as the couple rose, kissed, took the Bible, and walked out.

* * * * *

Back at the apartment, tables had been set up this way and that through the living and dining rooms. The guests filed in, and an elderly woman who seemed to know everyone ordered the guests tc their respective seats. I was seated next to Horst and his wife. The bride and groom found their way to what was the head table, and the pastor was seated next to them. It took a long time for everyone to find his place, and in the meantime the women brought out open bottles of Rumanian wine and set them on the tables. Theo got up to propose a toast, but the young pastor who had married him jumped right up behind him, saying, "Oh, no, you don't, young man! You can't propose a toast—not at your own wedding!"

This comment brought a roar of laughter and everybody stood up, not without some difficulty, as the pastor proposed a toast to the newlyweds. All raised their glasses and the wedding feast was under way.

The women now came in from the kitchen with tureens of soup, and after grace the meal began. While eating, everyone visited with each other except for a blond, robust, blue-eyed young man across the table from us. It was late in the meal when the food, the wine, and the heat in the room were having their effect that this man first spoke up.

Horst introduced the man as Klaus Rentschler, an incorrigible Communist.

Mr. Rentschler laughed back and made some comment about not needing to be corrected because he was already in the right. He then turned to me to ask how I liked the German Democratic Republic. I replied that in many ways I was favorably impressed, whereupon Mr. Rentschler began to give me a long history of the state's development in spite of the opposition of the Western warmongers and imperialists. I felt a little uneasy until I noted that Ilse was also embarrassed by his Party line spiel. I don't know whether it was the wine or just the closeness of the room, but I began to feel very warm.

"But look around you," Mr. Rentschler was saying, "what do you see? A new city. A new factory. New houses. New schools. Progress, everywhere progress. History is on the side of the German Democratic Republic."

Somebody down the table entered the conversation with the remark:

"Yes, we have now progressed to the point where if we hoard for a week we can get enough meat ahead for a wedding feast!"

Mr. Rentschler kept complete cool control of himself, but I noticed now that there was no humor in his remarks.

He answered: "The agriculture is collectivized. It had to be collectivized. It hurt, but if your child is sick, don't you take him to the doctor and give him a shot even if that shot hurts him?"

The answer was an old and trite one heard over and over again from the lips of those justifying totalitarian measures.

"What about old people?" I asked innocently, remembering that somewhere I had heard that the plight of the aged in the GDR was especially hard with the low pensions, shortage of medical help, and rationing of some foods.

Mr. Rentschler looked directly at me. His eyes fixed on my eyes. I noticed that Horst stopped eating. Our side of the table suddenly became quiet. Dead quiet.

It seemed like an eternity that we sat there, even though I knew it was only a handful of seconds. I became very warm. I had said something wrong. I had said something very wrong. What? Why? I felt a little ill, but still the blue eyes kept looking at me. Then I saw the lips begin to move and I heard the words:

"One cannot do everything at once. Our nation was completely destroyed at the end of the war—not that we didn't deserve it, but we were completely destroyed. In the process of rebuilding, some must work harder, some need more food. Others must sacrifice. Some of the old have had it harder than they deserve, but that is coming to an end now. Now those that age among us have homes to move to and doctors to care for them. No place in the world will people be better taken care of than in the GDR!"

The room was swimming. I was ill. I turned to Horst, completely ignoring Mr. Rentschler, and excused myself. I stood up. My feet were carrying me by chairs and talking, laughing people. I saw ahead of me the door to the balcony. My hands were opening it. My hands were closing it. It was cool. I stood inhaling the late afternoon coolness. The world began to pull together again. I became aware of the stillness. I noticed silly little things down below on the street. Only a few children were left outside playing. Lights were on in a few of the apartments. I breathed deeply, trying to remember that I was myself at a wedding in Neustadt in the German Democratic Republic.

Horst stood beside me. "Are you all right?" he asked. I said "Yes," and then explained that I was afraid the day had been too much for me.

"You couldn't know it," Horst began, "but only last week we buried Klaus Rentschler's mother. Klaus is one of the worst fanatics in Neustadt. Party loyal to the core. He climbed in the world, but his mother suffered. Just after the collectivization, during the years of shortage, she became ill. Her body was already weak from the ravages of the war. Klaus's father was an old Communist, one of the few. He was dead by 1942. Concentration camp. The mother raised the whole family. Six, I think. Klaus was the oldest. Became a top Party man. Big shot. How does the Bible put it: as to zeal a persecutor . . . ? She couldn't make it for the groceries. There was no phone to call a doctor. She lived to the last in a little cold-water flat. Then she died. She never lived to see the dawn of that great new day—for her—in the first farmers' and workers' state.

"Klaus came to Theo in the middle of the night and he broke. Those blond, blue-eyed North Germans are hard, but when they break they never break halfway. He set his jaw and asked Theo to ask the pastor to bury his mother. He stood there in the graveyard with his damn Party bonbon and gritted his teeth and held his face emotionless. Nobody in the Party offices dared to ask him why he had asked a Christian to bury his mother. They all came and just stood there as the Easter story was told. He stood there, his eyes cold as steel.

"Nobody wants him to hear that Easter story. The Party doesn't and the pious Christians don't. He's been the worst Red in this town. He's been on everyone's back with his trumpet-blowing and flag-waving. Wasn't old Ananias scared to death when the Lord told him that he had converted Paul, and Ananias was the one selected to minister to Paul? Just about lost Paul right there, old Ananias was so scared. Well, a lot of us were scared, too—at first. We looked at those blue eyes and the starch went right out of us. We were afraid to see a man saved. We were afraid to see a resurrection. We didn't want an Easter. But as sure as I stand here, the Lord is going to resurrect Klaus Rentschler and mighty will be that day."

Horst went back to the party and I stood alone again on the balcony. I wanted bells to ring in some distant church tower, but all I could hear was the half-hidden roar of the factory in the distance.

# ACKNOWLEDGMENTS

Otto Dibelius, "Ein Christ ist immer im Dienst"
Kreuz-Verlag, Stuttgart, 1961
English rights by Holt, Rinehart & Winston, "In the Service of the Lord"

Quote from the "Vorwort zur deutschen Ausgabe"
from Karl Marx and Friedrich Engels
Ausgewählte Schriften
Dietz Verlag Berlin 1961, German Democratic Republic

The Story "My Name Is Jack" comes from
"Bei uns in der Stadt"
Volk und Wissen Volkseigener Verlag, Berlin 1960, German Democratic Republic

Milan Machovec, "Marxismus und dialektische Theologie"
1965 EVZ-Verlag, Zurich, Switzerland

Adam Schaff, "Marxismus und das menschliche Individuum"
German rights, Europa Verlag-Wien
copyright Panstwowe Wydawnictwo Naukowe, Warszawa

Leszek Kolakowski, "Der Mensch ohne Alternative"
German rights, R. Piper & Co. Verlag, Munchen, Germany